June. 09

John Vaux

Middleton-on-Teesdale: Dent Bank

Jewels Beyond the Plough

A Celebration of Britain's Grasslands

Text by Richard Jefferson   *Illustrated by* John Davis

Quaking Grass

Upright Brome

Meadow Oat

Sweet Vernal

LANGFORD PRESS

Opposite

Portraits of grasses
Clockwise: Quaking grass, upright brome, sweet vernal grass and meadow oat.

First published 2012

© Richard Jefferson and John Davis

Langford Press, 10 New Road, Langtoft,
Peterborough PE 6 9 LE
Tel / Fax: 01778 341132
www.langford-press.co.uk
Email: sales@langford-press.co.uk

Printed & Bound by Healeys Printers, Ipswich, Suffolk.
Origination by Dean Hearn.

A cip Record for this book is available from the British Library.
ISBN 978-1-904078-41-8

Harvest mouse study
Harvest mice in rough, tall grassland with rushes and bent grasses. Harvest mouse numbers are thought to be declining.

John Davis: Inspiration

Sitting in a hay meadow in June with swallows skimming the grass tops and listening to a constant cascade of skylark song from somewhere high overhead, it didn't seem much like work! But the job in hand was to try and get down that intoxicating combination of colours from buttercups, knapweeds, greater burnet and a host of other wonderful plants that go to make up that rare thing, a hay meadow.

Or on southern downland, the scent of marjoram on a hot July day whilst trying to scribble chalk hill blues which shimmer past, only occasionally stopping.

It was a chance to focus my efforts in that brief season of summer and go to places that otherwise I would have missed, and to spend time in those seemingly timeless places. My only regret is that time did keep running out and I found myself having to dash to the next site!

I don't think I could pick a favourite, but Widdy bank Farm in Upper Teesdale came high up – listening to red grouse whilst sitting amongst orchids and hay rattle with snipe drumming and redshanks piping was pure magic.

Winter too had its special moments in a quieter time of year, especially downland under a fresh fall of snow with a passing fox, it's coat glowing against the white.

I am left with fond memories of some wonderful places.

Common blues and bumblebees
Common blue butterflies and bumblebees feeding on the flowers of common knapweed.

In a northern meadow with redshank
Redshank with chicks in a northern meadow. Cuckoo flower (light pink flowers) ragged robin
(dark pink flowers) and northern marsh orchid are prominent in the flower-rich sward.

Foreword

When I stand getting beaten by a blustery wind listening to the landscape conversing with the sky, watching far away birds bouncing off invisible blooms of air rolling up the escarpments of churning grass, feeling the pioneering prickles of rain exploding on my cheeks as dirty sheep stud the patches of brown between the green, the grip of nostalgia takes an easy hold. I like to remake Martin Down NNR, to imagine it through the eyes of refugees from Trafalgar, Naseby, Agincourt, to see what this seemingly ancient vista held for those Iron Age tribes who carved great twists of banks across its crests, I wonder at the carnage as the trees fell under bronze axes to inaugurate this manscape. And for all the space that falls away before me, allowing a perspective over a spread of three counties chalky hills, this is no place to entertain any fantasies of 'wilderness', this is our work, grassland old and new, from the relic downs to the fields of cereal. Some rich, some poor, all open, a habitat we walk on or over, not through, an ecotype with a simpler structure, with varied equivalents all over the world, from the Andes to the plains of Kansas, all the way to Africa, to the savannahs where we learned to walk. If our species has an ecological 'home' then it is grassland, and perhaps its some primal gene that seeds my affinity for such places. And I'm not alone because as this book reveals our need for and love of Grasslands is widespread and deep rooted.

Of course the structure of this landscape has been idealised by a plethora of artists and authors who have in many ways defined it as the 'countryside'. Ruskin, Wordsworth, Hardy et al, Constable and Stubbs have all offered us grasslands as part of the rural idyll. But the scale of their space may have shaped our visual desire for them but it largely overlooks their often incredible riches. To maximise this you need to get 'into' grassland and the easiest way to start is very simple... you lie down. No shrew or vole ever sees the horizon, perhaps no butterfly either, the ants, spiders, beetles and bugs live in it, not on it, to them it is a jungle with a myriad of micro spaces and surfaces where life can prosper. Peer through the towering stalks, poke amongst the deep detritus, crawl until your come to a glade where the air is warm and still and then turn and press your ear to the ground. Listen to an assortment of life you cannot even imagine. You can wander as lonely as a cloud and gaze beyond the Hay Wain but to meet grasshoppers and glow worms you need to get inside the habitat.

Two of Britain's most widely celebrated and fiercely protected habitats are grassland types, 'flower rich meadows' and 'downland'. Both are vestiges of redundant agricultural practices, rare because sadly they are no longer widely necessary to 'work' but relative to their modern counterparts they are a treasury of plants and animals. Fragments of both remain along with a great mix of other types, many now protected as nature reserves. You can visit these patches that time forgot and wonder at remarkable floral diversities, find exotics more beautiful than any old masters, stand in awe of banks of orchids, carpets of colour, and then revel in the delicious life histories of the weird and wonderful species which grow here safe from the sprays that produce the monotonous monocultures over the fence. And the list of pin-ups is profound, Fritillaries both plant and insect, waxcap fungi, Large Blues, Small Blues, burnet moths, yellow wagtails, Stone curlews, Skylarks...

Chris Packham

Small copper
The small copper butterfly occurs in a wide range of habitats including semi-natural grasslands that support its main food plants, namely common sorrel and sheep's sorrel. This colourful, diminutive butterfly, although remaining widespread in Great Britain, underwent a substantial decline during the last century.

Acknowledgements

Richard Jefferson

I would like to acknowledge the following colleagues, former tutors, friends and family who have provided information, commented on the text, provided assistance, support and encouragement or have been instrumental in influencing my thinking on the ecology and conservation of our wildlflower-rich grasslands.

Isabel Alonso	The late Charlie Gibson	Keith Kirby	Steve Peel	Ken Roy
Stewart Angus	David Gowing	Ian Langford	Jane Phillips	David Sheppard
John Bingham	Phil Grice	Jane MacKintosh	Clare Pinches	Roger Smith
Tim Blackstock	Elinor Gwynn	David Martin	Keith Porter	The late David Stevens
Alan Booth	Steve Hallam	Chris McCarty	Sarah Priest	Stuart Smith
Peter Brotherton	John Hopkins	Gavin Measures	Richard Pywell	Jill Sutcliffe
Andy Brown	Phil Horton	Nick Michael	Donna Radley	Jerry Tallowin
Val Brown	Audra Hurst	Tony Mitchell-Jones	Mick Rebane	Michael Usher
John Creedy	Robert Jefferson	Richard Moles	Richard Rafe	Stephen Ward
Alistair Crowle	Roger Key	Derek Moore	Carrie Rimes	Jon Webb
Iain Diack	Rosy Key	Vicky Morgan	Heather Robertson	Helen Williams
Paul Evans	Rick Keymer	Owen Mountford	John Rodwell	Hazel Woodward
Vin Fleming	Miles King	Matthew Oates	Fytton Rowland	

Special thanks are due to Jill Sutcliffe for providing support and encouragement throughout the preparation of the book. Mark Howarth and Jill also kindly hosted three progress meetings at their wonderful farmhouse in West Sussex. This included the provision of splendid food and refreshments! Brigid Newland and Jill Sutcliffe kindly read through all of the text and made some changes and suggestions resulting in considerable improvement.

I would like to acknowledge the support of Natural England in allowing me some time to write the text. Also thanks are due to staff in Countryside Council for Wales and Scottish Natural Heritage for commenting on sections of text and supplying information.

I dedicate the book to the memory of my father, Peter Jefferson, who was wholly responsible for initiating my lifelong interest in plants and natural history. Also thanks are due to my mother, Betty Kitchen, who has supported and enthused me throughout my career.

John Davis

I would like to thank the following friends and family:
Jill Sutcliffe for her much valued support, encouragement and friendship over many years. Richard Williamson, former warden of Kingley Vale National Nature Reserve, for his huge knowledge of downland wildlife especially, and, as an inspiration with his boundless enthusiasm and very fine writing. Ann Griffiths, former ecologist with West Sussex County Council, for her depth of knowledge of chalk grassland, plants and their conservation. And of course, my wife Caroline, for turning a blind eye and letting me swan about the countryside pretending that I was in fact, working hard!

Permissions

The publisher and authors would like to thank WILD*guides* for permission to reproduce the landscape through the ages illustrations which first appeared in Wilson, P. & King, M. 2003 *Arable plants – a field guide*. WILD*guides*

Male and female linnets
Linnets are a widespread seed-feeding species found on farmland. They eat the seeds of a wide variety of plants but, in particular, arable weeds. However, they will also feed on the seeds of grassland plants such as buttercups, common cats-ear, meadowsweet and thistles. They breed in any open habitat that has a scatter of low shrubs such as gorse.

Grey Ferguson tractor
The grey Ferguson tractor, first manufactured in 1946, was the machine that replaced the horse on many British farms during the 1940s. It was often affectionately known as the Little or Wee Grey Fergie. This tractor was used in grassland and arable farming. As far as wildflower-rich grasslands are concerned, this tractor was used for hay cutting, handling hay, baling and the spreading of farmyard manure. Although production ceased in 1956 with the development of newer models, there are many still in use. The story of the Grey Ferguson is recounted in The Ferguson Tractor Story by Stuart Gibbard.

Contents

Modern tractor boom spraying
As a contrast to the grey Ferguson, this picture shows a modern tractor boom spraying grassland! Although, modern tractors and equipment are widely used for managing wildflower-rich grasslands, they are often unsuitable for use in small fields.

Preface

This book is a celebration of Britain's wildflower grasslands. The illustrations capture the beauty of grassland landscapes with their rich flora and fauna. A quick glance shows the remarkable range of plants and animals associated with wildflower grasslands. Orchids, cowslips, buttercups, fritillaries, pasque flowers, curlews, lapwings, butterflies, grasshoppers, waxcap fungi, mosses and lichens all feature prominently.

It is hoped that this book will provide an inspiration and raise awareness of the beauty and value to society of our wildflower-rich grasslands.

Introduction

Over the last 5,000 years a combination of the actions of people, their domesticated animals and the prevailing environment have combined to produce grasslands in Britain where previously there would have been mostly woodland. Grasslands have been instrumental in the provision of food (meat and milk from livestock) and clothing (through the production of leather and wool). Grassland, though, has not just provided us with some means of survival: through the ages, it has contributed greatly to our leisure and cultural life, the latter being expressed in poetry, prose and art. William Shakespeare describes meadows ("the even mead") in Henry V and John Clare, the Northamptonshire rural Romantic poet, refers to the heaths around his

home, which were areas of grassland, with some gorse and heather. John Constable painted Salisbury Cathedral in its setting of water-meadows and William Nicholson "The Dandelion Field" seemingly while lying in the grass.

"The even mead, that erst brought sweetly forth
The freckled cowslip, burnet, and green clover,
Wanting the scythe, all uncorrected, rank,
Conceives by idleness, and nothing teems
But hateful docks, rough thistles, kecksies, burs,
Losing both beauty and utility"
HENRY V WILLIAM SHAKESPEARE: 1599

Parks and lawns provide green space in towns and cities for informal amenity activities. A number of popular sports such as soccer, rugby, cricket and tennis have their origins on grass and this natural medium continues to be the preferred surface in many cases. More recently, the increased popularity of gardening to attract wildlife has seen the creation of small flower-rich meadows in people's gardens.

What is grassland?

Grassland is low-growing vegetation that normally contains a high cover of grasses (*Graminae*) (see text boxes) but it will often also contain other species of plants depending on its history and management.

Mole
Moles thrive in meadows and pastures where they feed on soil invertebrates, in particular earthworms.

Grasses (Family Poaceae)

Grasses fall within the flowering plants known as the Angiosperms. They first appeared in the Cretaceous period around 70 million years ago. They generally have long, narrow leaves arranged in two rows alternating one with another on a cylindrical stem. The flowers are often small and inconspicuous and are pollinated by wind. They are monocotyledons, meaning that on germination the seed embryo produces only one seed leaf compared to two in dicotyledons.

It is estimated that there are about 10,000 species of grasses in the world and around 900 species in Europe. In Britain there are around 178 species (excluding cultivated species, hybrids and sub-species), of which 118 species are considered native.

Grasses are found in virtually all habitats and can be annual (complete life cycle in a single year), biennial (complete life cycle within two years), or perennial (lives for more than two years). British grasses range in size from a few centimetres in height, such as early sand grass (*Mibora minima*), to several metres (e.g. common reed (*Phragmites australis*)), but worldwide the largest grasses are the bamboos with some tropical species attaining heights of up to 30 metres. Grasses also vary considerably in their growth form, ranging from species that form dense tussocks (e.g. tufted hair-grass [*Deschampsia cespitosa*]) to those that form creeping mats (e.g. creeping soft grass [*Holcus mollis*]). The success of grasses in grassland is due to the ability of their leaves to grow continuously from the base so that if they are grazed or cut they simply regenerate fresh green tissue.

Human societies over the millennia have relied on grasses as staple foodstuffs and forage for domesticated livestock. Five of the world's 12 key crops – wheat, barley, rice, maize (corn) and sorghum – are grasses. These five cereals account for over half of all calories consumed by humans. Sugar cane is also grown as a source of sugar. In Europe and North America, a few perennial grasses (e.g. elephant grass (*Pennisetum purpureum*) are used as renewable bioenergy sources. In the last few hundred years, grassland has formed the playing surface for popular sports such as football, golf and cricket and provided a resource for informal amenity and recreation, especially the green spaces in towns and cities. Grassland lawns associated with dwellings probably date from the medieval period and, as well as being decorative, are used for informal recreation.

The vast majority of grassland in Britain has been sown with varieties of perennial rye-grass (*Lolium perenne*) and white clover (*Trifolium repens*) bred specifically for agricultural production. These so-called improved grasslands are of very limited value for wildlife, although they do provide breeding and feeding areas for certain farmland birds. With some modification to their management they could, though, include more plants and provide better breeding or feeding opportunities, particularly for invertebrates, mammals and birds.

Scope of the book

This book concentrates on and celebrates Britain's semi-natural or wildflower grasslands which are made up of unsown, wild native plants. Historically, i.e. probably prior to the 20th Century, most agricultural grasslands would have been broadly semi-natural in character. Semi-natural grassland contains many species of flowering plants, mosses, liverworts and fungi. They are termed semi-natural as, in the absence of mowing and grazing undertaken for agriculture and more recently additionally for nature conservation, most would revert to woodland within a few decades. Semi-natural grasslands are normally very rich in plant species, typically exceeding fifteen species in a square metre. For some chalk and limestone grasslands, this can exceed forty species per square metre.

One of the difficulties that have faced their conservation is that there has been little appreciation that the more valuable wildlife-rich grasslands, when seen from a distance, are not entirely bright green but are generally a range of duller shades of green or even brown at certain times of the year. Thus, this has led to a perception that the presence of bright green grassland in the countryside equates to general environmental well-being!

The key to sustaining the wildlife value of most semi-natural grasslands is regular management by cutting and grazing with no or minimal addition of fertilisers. Wildlife value can be substantially diminished by the application of herbicides, artificial fertilisers or heavy dressings of manures or slurry. These practices are used to improve or increase value for agricultural production and results in a reduction in the number and variety of wildflowers characteristic of these grasslands. This is because fertilisers encourage more vigorous species to increase and the wildflower species cannot compete and eventually decrease or disappear.

Two other types of grassland that are semi-improved have been included in the book as they have significant wildlife or heritage value. These are coastal and flood plain grazing marsh, and water meadows.

Semi-improved grasslands were formerly semi-natural grasslands that have since been subjected to some agricultural improvement, especially through the application of moderate amounts of artificial fertilisers or heavy dressings of manures. Typically such grasslands are moderately rich in plant species (8-15 species in a square metre), but there is usually an increased cover of species (such as various grasses, especially perennial rye-grass and Yorkshire fog (*Holcus lanatus*), plus white clover) which thrive in more nutrient-rich conditions.

Apart from grazing marshes and water meadows, other areas of semi-improved grasslands are of value for wildlife, especially in areas of the country where there is very little semi-natural grassland. They may also provide important breeding or feeding areas for farmland birds.

The large tracts of semi-natural grassland in the uplands occurring on acidic rocks such as sandstones (upland acid grassland) and not enclosed by fences or walls are not covered in this book. This grassland type is not normally of high wildlife interest in its own right, as it is dominated by a few grasses and rushes and is often poor in other flowering plants. Upland acid grassland is often the product of over-grazing of moorland heath which is dominated by heather (*Calluna vulgaris*) with lesser amounts of bilberry (*Vaccinium myrtillus*).

Extent and trends

In the UK, agricultural land covers about 75% of the land area, of which around 40% is grassland,

Definitions

Flowering plants (flowers)

Plants (Angiosperms) that have reproductive units known as flowers. These comprise the male stamens and the carpel (the structure that bears and encloses the female parts namely the ovary, styles and stigma). In many cases, flowers may also have other structures such as petals and sepals. Specifically excludes ferns, horsetails, mosses, liverworts, stoneworts and conifers but includes grasses, sedges and rushes.

Grassland

Land which is predominantly covered by grass species (Graminae) but not exclusively
so: semi-natural grassland contains many other flowering plants, mosses, liverworts and fungi. Trees are the natural vegetation cover over most of Britain given its current climate and, except in those places which are too steep, too dry or too high for trees or are grazed by wild herbivores, grassland would eventually become tree-covered in the absence of cutting or grazing.

Improved grassland

Grassland that has been sown with varieties of grasses (especially perennial rye-grass and timothy (*Phleum pratense*)) and white clover bred specifically for agricultural production. These grasslands contain no or few other plant species and so are mostly of very limited value for wildlife. Note that these grasslands are "improved" for intensive agricultural purposes but not for wildlife!

Semi-improved grassland

Former semi-natural grassland that has been subjected to some kind of agricultural improvement especially through the application of moderate amounts of artificial fertilisers or heavy dressings of manures. Typically such grasslands are moderately rich in plant species (8-15 species in a square metre) but there is usually an increased cover of species which thrive in more nutrient-rich conditions such as various grasses, especially perennial rye-grass and Yorkshire fog, plus white clover.

Semi-natural grassland

Grassland which is composed of unsown, wild native plants - normally a mixture of grasses, herbaceous wildflowers, sedges, rushes and mosses. They are termed semi-natural as, in the absence of mowing and grazing, most would revert to scrub and woodland in a few decades. Their wildlife value can be substantially diminished by the application of herbicides, artificial fertilisers or heavy dressings of manures or slurry.

Unimproved grassland

Synonymous with semi-natural grassland.

excluding rough grazing. However, less than 1% of the total land area comprises wildflower-rich semi-natural grassland (excluding upland acid grassland). Of the total area of grassland (excluding rough grazing), probably around 2% comprises wildflower-rich semi-natural grassland. This remaining area equates to an area roughly the size of County Durham. Table 1 provides the most recent estimates for the main types of semi-natural grassland occurring in Great Britain.

As far as the total area of all grassland is concerned, the general long-term trend throughout most of the 20th Century has been one of decreasing grassland and increasing arable land, prompted largely by the need for increased self-reliance for food during World War II. However, from the late 1990s until recently, the overall area of grassland increased. This trend has recently started to reverse.

There have been significant historical losses of wildflower-rich grassland particularly in the lowlands. Between 1930 and 1984 there was a 97% loss in England and Wales. Local surveys undertaken by County Wildlife Trusts and other bodies during the 1980s and 1990s also revealed losses of grassland at high rates, principally due to agricultural improvement. In Derbyshire, 91% of wildflower grasslands which had existed in 1983 had disappeared by 1999, whilst a study of hay meadows in Northamptonshire revealed a loss to agricultural improvement of 11% of sites since 1980, with a further 3% partly destroyed. More recently, a national survey of 500 important grassland sites with no statutory protection, undertaken in 2002 and 2003 revealed that one in four sites now most resembled agriculturally improved grassland types, indicating an actual loss of wildlife-rich grassland between 1980 and 2003. The survey revealed that management neglect, including under-grazing, was the main cause of the unfavourable condition of calcareous and acidic grassland. In contrast, past or current agricultural intensification (e.g. nutrient enrichment from fertilisers, drainage, re-seeding, over-grazing) was the main cause of unfavourable condition in both types of meadows, such that the swards typically lacked key plant species characteristic of such grasslands.

However, although the speed of such losses was very much a post World War II phenomenon, the extract from the Flora of Cambridgeshire, demonstrates that conversion of semi-natural grassland to arable was occurring in the 19th Century!

There is very little recorded about the losses of grassland of high wildlife value (largely calcareous [limestone] grassland) in the uplands. However, in contrast, on open or unenclosed grasslands in the uplands, the issue is more to do with degradation through unsympathetic management practices such as too heavy grazing or the use of fertilisers leading to a reduction in the number and diversity

C.C. Babington, Flora of Cambridgeshire, 1860

Until recently (within 60 years) most of the chalk district was open and covered with a beautiful coating of turf, profusely decorated with *Anemone pulsatilla* [Pasque flower], *Astragalus hypoglottis* [Purple milk vetch], and other interesting plants. It is now converted into arable land, and its peculiar plants mostly confined to small waste spots by road-sides, pits, and the very few banks which are too steep for the plough. Thus many species which were formerly abundant have become rare; so rare as to have caused an unjust suspicion of their not really being natives to arise in the minds of some modern botanists. Even the tumuli, entrenchments and other interesting works of the ancient inhabitants have seldom escaped the rapacity of the modern agriculturalist, who too frequently looks upon the native plants of the country as weeds, and its antiquities as deformities.

of wildflowers, rather than outright loss. There was a temporary cessation of grazing in some areas of the north Pennine uplands in 2001 after the foot and mouth disease outbreak. There was subsequently a reduction in grazing pressure. These two events have resulted in the expansion of a number of plant species characteristic of upland semi-natural habitats, including increased amounts of flowering. This is eloquently described by Roberts (2010) in an article in the British Wildlife magazine.

Current and future prospects

Over the last few decades, a range of measures have substantially contributed to protecting, conserving and enhancing our wildflower-rich grasslands for future generations. These include designation of the most important grasslands as statutory Sites of Special Scientific Interest (SSSI),

Table 1: Estimates of the current extent of grasslands of wildlife or heritage value in Great Britain

Grassland type	Estimated area (ha)
Calcareous grassland (including chalk & limestone grassland)	62, 294
Lowland acid grassland	60,972
Old meadows and pastures	9,585
Marshy grassland	60,473
Coastal and flood plain grazing marsh	211,218
Machair	17,500 [1]
Water meadows	130 [2]
Total	422,172

[1] Source: Stewart Angus, Scottish Natural Heritage.
[2] This figure relates to the current area of working water meadows. Everard (2005) mentions that 40, 500 ha of water meadow were constructed in England between the early 17th and 19th centuries demonstrating the decline in this specialised grassland management system.

the introduction and operation of voluntary agri-environment schemes[1], the establishment of grassland nature reserves and other land-use policy instruments.

However, although there have been many positive achievements, much remains to be done, as current evidence shows that many semi-natural grasslands in Great Britain are in unfavourable condition. This is particularly the case for grasslands that are not designated as SSSI. In the lowlands, unfavourable condition is primarily due to the cessation of management by grazing and /or cutting, and in some cases to the detrimental impacts of nutrient inputs from agricultural or atmospheric sources. Also, direct losses due to agricultural intensification and residential development continue to occur, albeit at lower rates compared to the recent past. In contrast, in the uplands, the main issues are over-grazing and nutrient additions from fertilisers or from atmospheric deposition.

Climate change is likely to have an impact on the species composition and management of some wildflower-rich grasslands, particularly those grasslands that support species which prefer cool, moist environments. Reducing the impact of climate change on the wildlife of our semi-natural grasslands will require, in particular, the conservation of existing grassland sites and the enlargement and linking of existing areas through the creation of new grassland habitat or the restoration of semi-improved grasslands.

If the overall wildlife condition of grasslands is to improve, the continued application and expansion of current conservation land-use measures will be necessary.

In addition, the importance of semi-natural grasslands in providing services for society needs to be further promoted to help to ensure that a strong case is made for their conservation for future generations.

Firstly, they are heritage assets with high intrinsic appeal and scientific value. There is also increasing evidence that access to nature such as provided by wildflower-rich grasslands can have benefits for people's health and wellbeing.

Such grasslands also can provide economic services such as flood alleviation (flood-plain grasslands), soil conservation, the improvement of water quality via improved nutrient retention, carbon storage – which helps to mitigate climate change – and the provision of benefits for agriculture, such as the supply of beneficial insects for pollination and pest control in agricultural crops.

[1] Agri-environment scheme is a term used to describe national (or local) schemes that pay farmers to farm in an environmentally sensitive manner.

Stone Age

Evolution of the landscape through the ages illustrations

Neolithic (Stone Age), Bronze Age, Roman, Mediaeval. Compare with the modern landscape (pages 166-167) Modern farming-with wildlife, (pages 164-165) Modern farming-without wildlife. These illustrations show the evolution of a typical farmed chalk landscape of scarp slope and vale through the ages, commencing with the Neolithic and culminating in the present day landscape. The last two illustrations (pages 164-167) show two contrasting scenes, firstly a recent farmed landscape where there is little accommodation for wildlife and secondly a modern landscape where opportunities to conserve wildlife have been taken. These illustrations first appeared in the Arable plants – a field guide published in 2003 [see http://www.arableplants.fieldguide.co.uk/]. See also http://www.arableplants.org.uk/ for more information on the conservation and ecology of arable plants.

Bronze Age

Iron Age

Roman times

Medieval

Hay making in the
Yorkshire Dales.

Old meadows and pastures

Old meadows and pastures occur on well-drained or moist soils that are neither very acid nor very lime-rich (neutral), within enclosed field systems throughout the UK, normally below 300m. They may be managed as hay meadow or as pasture.

In general, these meadows and pastures are composed of a varied mixture of herbs, grasses and sedges with herbaceous species comprising a relatively high proportion of the sward.

Flower-rich old meadows and pastures are among our most treasured wildlife habitats and until the 1960s they were a widespread feature of the British countryside. Richard Mabey captured the essence of these meadows in his book *The Common Ground: a place for nature in Britain's future?*

If we were to look for an indicator *habitat*, the feature of farms most sensitive to the combined pressures of ploughing, drainage and chemical dressing, I think it would have to be the traditional hay meadow...I must admit that, until I had actually seen one, I wondered whether such places ever really existed outside our stubbornly romantic rural fantasies. My first encounter, when it finally happened... put paid to any such doubts. It was one of those experiences that was the more vivid for being, in many ways, so unexpected: a stroll across a flowerless pasture, a gap in the hedge, and then, suddenly, this brilliant field lapped with layers of colour and movement – yellow hay-rattle, red betony, purple knapweeds and orchids, the swaying cream umbels of pepper-saxifrage, and butterflies so dense and vibrant above the flowers that it was hard to tell them from the heat-haze. On the far side of the meadow they had started cutting the hay, and the air was full of the heavy smell of new-mown grass and the sharper scents of meadow-sweet and burnet.

I had, quite certainly, not seen anything like this in my lifetime. Yet, so indelible is the impression of these flowery meadows on our folk memory, that every detail was familiar to me. Hay-plots like this were once as important and characteristic a feature of the village agricultural system as the open field and the coppice wood.

Following page
Hay meadow, Dent Bank, Upper Teesdale
This colourful upland hay meadow forms part of the Middle Side and Stonygill meadows complex in Upper Teesdale, County Durham. The showy blue flowers of meadow cranesbill are visible on the edge of the meadow and in the foreground. This plant rarely occurs in meadows as it would seem that it is intolerant of grazing. It is, though, widespread in habitats that are ungrazed such as roadside verges and riversides. The compact crimson flowers of great burnet are also in evidence in the sward. The first part of the Latin name of this species *Sanguis* (blood) and *sorba* (absorb) points to its medicinal use – to staunch the flow of blood, including nosebleeds. It can also be used to treat burns and insect bites and the leaves can be eaten in salads; they taste like cucumber!

Middleton-on-Teesdale: DENT BANK

June: 09

John Davi-

late Summer in a wea

den Meadow . 'Badlands', W. Sussex   17 September . 08

John Davis

Wealden hay meadow in autumn
The 'Badlands', part of the Mens
National Nature Reserve, West
Sussex – a lowland hay meadow in
the Weald in late summer. Flowers
in the foreground include the purple-
flowered devil's-bit scabious and
the crimson flowers of common
knapweed and betony. A tall spike
of marsh thistle is very prominent.

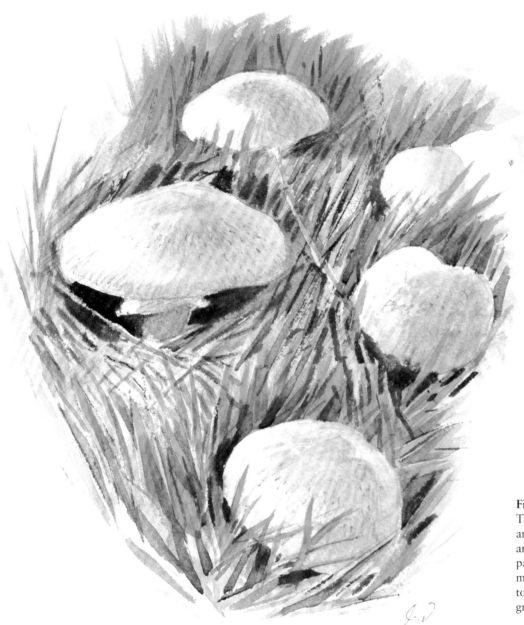

Field mushrooms
The familiar field mushroom has pink gills and is very good to eat! Field mushrooms are common in semi-natural meadows and pastures. In general, these grasslands support many more species of mushrooms and toadstools than agriculturally-improved grasslands.

Characteristic plant species include common knapweed (*Centaurea nigra*), ox-eye daisy (*Leucanthemun vulgare*), bird's foot trefoil (*Lotus corniculatus*), lady's bedstraw (*Galium verum*), common sorrel (*Rumex acetosa*) yellow meadow vetchling (*Lathyrus pratensis*), meadow buttercup (*Ranunculus acris*), cowslip (*Primula veris*), and the grasses crested dog's tail (*Cynosurus cristatus*), quaking grass (*Briza media*), sweet vernal grass (*Anthoxanthum odoratum*), yellow oat-grass (*Trisetum flavescens*), red fescue (*Festuca rubra*) and common bent (*Agrostis capillaris*).

Two distinctive types are maintained by hay meadow management. One type is characteristic of flat land adjacent to lowland rivers and streams, largely in England, and is often referred to as flood or alluvial meadow. The other occurs in the bottom of or on the sides of upland valleys in the northern Pennines, the Lake District and on riverbanks in Scotland. These are often referred to as upland or northern hay meadows.

Flood meadows, in addition to the plant species listed above, may contain species often typical of damper habitats such as great burnet (*Sanguisorba officinalis*), meadowsweet (*Filipendula ulmaria*), common meadow rue (*Thalictrum flavum*) and, very occasionally, meadow thistle (*Cirsium dissectum*).

Typical species that characterise upland hay meadows include wood cranesbill (*Geranium sylvaticum*), melancholy thistle (*Cirsium heterophyllum*), pignut, (*Conopodium majus*), lady's mantles (*Alchemilla* spp), and, in wetter types, globeflower (*Trollius europaeus*), marsh marigold (*Caltha palustris*) and marsh hawksbeard (*Crepis paludosa*).

Skylark
Skylark in Upper Teesdale, Durham. Snipe were also drumming in the vicinity at the time this painting was composed. This peculiar "bleating" sound is created when the outer tail feathers of the fanned tail are twisted to make an angle with the other feathers whereupon the bird dives at speed until the air passing over the plumage creates the drumming noise.

John Davis

Derwent Ings: Aughton church looking south:
June 23rd.09

Previous page
Derwent Ings, Aughton
Flood meadows at Aughton, Derwent Ings, North Yorkshire. The meadow in the foreground has an abundance of meadowsweet which has creamy white flowers with a heavy scent. The Norman All Saints Church, Aughton overlooks the Ings and lies adjacent to earthworks of a motte and bailey castle and the moated site of the manor house of the Aske family. On the exterior church wall there is a carving of a newt (or Asker in Old English). This is said to be the emblem of Robert Aske who set out from here in 1536 to lead the Pilgrimage of Grace against the religious reforms of Henry VIII.

Green-winged Orchids

Green winged orchids
Green winged orchids. This orchid is typical of old meadows and pastures. It was once widespread but has declined greatly over the last fifty years due to the loss of semi-natural grasslands to agricultural intensification.

The wildlife value of old meadows and pastures derives from the rich mix of mostly widespread species as opposed to the occurrence of rare or threatened species. However, there are a number of threatened plants associated with the habitat including sulphur clover (*Trifolium ochroleucon*), meadow saffron (*Colchicum autumnale*), snake's head fritillary (*Fritillaria meleagris*), green-winged orchid (*Orchis morio*) and northern hawk's-beard (*Crepis mollis*).

Green-winged orchids, Lighter's field
A magnificent display of green-winged orchids at Bosham Hoe, West Sussex.

Green-winged Orchids at Lighters field Bosham Hoe
27 April. 09

Upland hay meadows, in conjunction with other habitats of the upland landscape, provide important nesting and feeding habitat for various waders, notably redshank (*Tringa totanus*), lapwing (*Vanellus vanellus*), snipe (*Gallinago gallinago*), oystercatcher (*Haematopus ostralegus*) and curlew (*Numenius arquata*). In addition, small perching birds, such as yellow wagtail (*Motacilla flava*), skylark (*Alauda arvensis*), meadow pipit (*Anthus pratensis*), linnet (*Carduelis cannabina*) and twite (*Acanthis flavirostris*) are closely associated with hay meadows for either feeding or breeding.

Larger flood meadows, such as those associated with the lower reaches of the Yorkshire river Derwent, can support important populations of breeding wading birds and wintering wildfowl. Such grassland also provides important breeding sites for the skylark and the corn bunting (*Emberiza calandra*), both of which have undergone a rapid decline over the last 25 years.

Previous page
Fritillaries, North Meadow
North Meadow National Nature Reserve in the Thames valley in Wiltshire consists of an extensive area of flower-rich flood meadow, one of Britain's rarest types of semi-natural grassland. It has been estimated that there is less than 1500 hectares of this grassland remaining in Great Britain. In late April, the meadow is ablaze with the blooms of hundreds of thousands of snake's head fritillaries. This is a threatened plant species and there are now fewer than twenty native sites in England that have more than 100 plants.

The corncrake (*Crex crex*) was once a common and widespread summer visitor to Great Britain. It breeds in late-cut hay meadows and other tall vegetation. It has declined dramatically in last 150 years due to agricultural intensification. The decline has been caused by changes in grassland management. In particular, this has been due to increasing mechanisation and speed of grass cutting and, since 1945, the shift from hay making to silage production with earlier and multiple cutting. In Great Britain, it is confined to the Scottish Hebrides and Argyll Islands where it breeds on the machair.

There is now a programme of conservation that aims to reverse the decline of this species in Great Britain including a trial re-introduction of the bird in one of its former haunts in eastern England.

The day-flying chimney sweeper moth (*Odezia atrata*) may occur in old meadows and pastures that have pignut, the moth's larval food plant. This moth is unmistakable as it is almost entirely sooty black.

chimney-sweep moth and pignut

Chimney sweep moth
Chimney sweep moth on pignut, the larval food plant. This combination is for illustrative purposes as the flight period of the moth (June and July) does not normally overlap with pignut in full flower (April to May).

Hay and hay making:
its role in the conservation of wildflower-rich old hay meadows.

The wildlife value of wildflower-rich meadows is sustained by a summer cut for hay followed by grazing. Prior to our interest in the wildlife of these meadows, particularly after World War II, their main raison d'être was as a source of hay used as winter feed or fodder for livestock production. Hay is dried grass/herbage cut from a meadow in summer, which is usually baled and then stored for later use. There has been a dramatic decline in the volume of field-cured hay made in Great Britain in the latter half of the 20th Century with hay being replaced by silage. Silage is a grass or other forage crop harvested in a green state that is subsequently preserved or ensiled by fermentation in an airtight environment such as in a silo, a clamp or as bales wrapped in plastic[1]. Silage is now the main system for producing conserved grass for winter livestock feed, especially on agriculturally-improved grasslands. For example, in Scotland, the north-west Highlands and Islands are now the last outpost of traditional hay making in the country.

Hay requires a rapid removal of moisture from the cut herbage to a level that is low enough (aiming for approximately 85% Dry Matter (DM)) to allow the grass to be stored in a suitable condition for winter feeding. In Great Britain, the relatively moist cool climate means that hay needs a lengthy drying period, typically 3-5 days in the field prior to baling. The unpredictability of British summers thus makes hay making an uncertain process! Rain during hay making reduces hay quality for example through fungal infection of the cut hay. In contrast, silage can be made much more rapidly and is much less weather-dependent as once cut it can be ensiled immediately (at perhaps 20% DM) or after wilting, often to 25-50% DM. Thus, it is easy to see why hay making has declined and there has been a increase in grass preservation as silage.

The increase in silage at the expense of hay has been driven by the fact that little drying is required so herbage can be cut at an earlier (wetter) growth stage when it has a higher digestibility. The nutritive value of silage depends not only on this but also the speed and stability of the fermentation. This is improved by ensiling grasses with a high content of sugars and other soluble carbohydrates, typically ryegrasses. Thus silage making is associated with grassland intensification which often involves ploughing of existing grassland fields, re-seeding with perennial rye-grass and regular dressing of artificial fertilisers to promote high productivity of highest quality forage for use in intensive livestock systems. High crop yields, from up to three grass cuts a year, may be required to justify the machinery, labour and fuel costs associated with silage making. The shift to silage has resulted in losses of, and degradation of wildflower-rich meadows and their associated fauna. This has been caused by direct losses due to ploughing and re-seeding. In addition, many former wildflower-rich meadows have had their wildlife value reduced by heavy applications of fertiliser coupled with earlier cutting. The latter may be disastrous for breeding birds using meadows if it occurs before chicks have fledged. Also, certain characteristic plants may be adversely affected, especially early-flowering annual species which need to produce seed to persist.

1 For a fuller definition, see glossary of grassland terms.

Muker Meadows, Swaledale
Flower-rich upland hay meadows near Muker in Upper Swaledale, North Yorkshire. This landscape, with its flowery meadows in small fields bounded by drystone walls and dotted with stone hay barns, is a major attraction for visitors to the Yorkshire Dales National Park. The purple-flowered wood crane's-bill in the foreground is a characteristic plant of upland hay meadows in England and Scotland. These upland meadows are one of the rarest types of grassland in Great Britain and it has been estimated that less than 1,000 hectares now remain.

Meadows at Mukar

25 June .09

John Jarvis

High Brae Pasture, near Ingleborough
An upland pastoral scene at High Brae, near Ingleborough, North Yorkshire. The meadow in the foreground contains a variety of plants including the russet-coloured common sorrel and the yellow-flowered yellow rattle, a plant that is partially parasitic on various grasses and legumes.

John Davis

High Brae Pasture: near Ingleborough
25 June '09

Meadows at Starbotton, Wharfedale
A flowery upland hay meadow near Starbotton in
Wharfedale, Yorkshire Dales National Park.

Star Bottom – Kettlewell
John Davis   25 June '09

Widdy bank Farm, Upper Teesdale
A flower-rich upland hay meadow in the valley of the River Tees near Widdy bank Farm, Upper Teesdale, County Durham. Cow Green Reservoir is just upstream from here. The meadow is full of flowers including buttercups, red clover and common sorrel. The north Pennines, including Upper Teesdale, are an exceptionally important area for breeding waders, especially lapwing, curlew, snipe and redshank (the last two species are pictured).

Meadow near Amberley, West Sussex
A meadow near Amberley, West Sussex with abundant meadow buttercup. The hawthorn in the background is in full bloom. This may blossom provides an important nectar source for insects.

Calcareous (including chalk and limestone) grasslands

Woodlark
The woodlark is a species that has undergone a large decline in numbers over the last 100 years. It has thus been the focus of recent conservation management programmes. Woodlarks breed in a variety of habitats including dry grassland, heathland and, increasingly, clear-felled and replanted conifer plantations. It prefers a mosaic of short vegetation, bare ground, taller vegetation and scattered trees.

Calcareous grassland is a feature of some of Britain's most attractive landscapes such as the rolling chalk downland of southern England, the limestone gorges, hills and crags of the Mendips in Somerset, the coastal headlands of the North Wales coast, the limestone country of the Yorkshire Dales and Cumbria, and the mountains of the Breadalbane area in the Scottish Highlands.

One of the most vivid descriptions of southern English chalk downland was written by W.H. Hudson, Argentinian-born author and naturalist, in *Nature in Downland*, published in 1900

The Downs (Sussex) are nowhere tame, but I seldom care to loiter long in their cultivated parts. It seems better to get away... to walk on the turf. This turf is composed of small grasses and clovers mixed with a great variety of creeping herbs, some exceedingly small. In a space of one square foot of ground, a dozen or twenty or more species of plants may be counted, and in turning up a piece of turf the innumerable fibrous interwoven roots have the appearance of cocoa-nut matting. It is indeed this thick layer of interlaced fibres that gives the turf its springiness, and makes it so delightful to walk upon. It is fragrant, too. The air, especially in the evening of a hot spring day, is full of a fresh herby smell, to which many minute aromatic plants contribute...The vegetation has the appearance of a beautiful tapestry worked in various shades of green, roughened with the slender dry bents standing out like pale yellow thread-ends from the green texture; flecked, and in places splashed with brilliant colour - red, purple, blue, and yellow. Or if you look at the flowers with the sun before you they appear like shining gems sewn in the fabric and forming an irregular pattern...Commonest in spring, when yellow flowers most abound, is the bird-foot trefoil. The wee fairy yellow trefoil is common too; and clovers red and clovers white; and the kidney vetch, with curious embossed or jewelled flower-heads. Creeping rock-rose with soft, silky petals, and clustered bell-flower, deep blue, looking like Canterbury bells picked from their stalk and scattered about on the grass. Crane's-bill and musky stork's-bill- mere specks of red: little round-leaved mint, a faint misty purple; and the scented plantain, its leaves like leaves cut out of green cloth, pressed flat and sewn upon a green fabric. Rest-harrow, very dark green on a light green turf, with minute pink and white butterfly blossoms. Woodruff, round and among the furze bushes, like powdery snow newly fallen on the green earth: the curiously named squinancy-wort, exceeding small and fragrant, blooming all over the turfy downs, here white, there rose-red, or deep red, or purple, so variable is it in colour...Butterflies are abundant...Most abundant is the little pale blue of the chalk downs...Sitting on the grass you can sometimes count as many as thirty or forty fluttering about in sight and near you at one time. It is curious to note that the hue of the sky and atmosphere on this insect's wings appears to have "entered his soul," to make him more aerial in habits, more light-hearted and playful in disposition than his other-coloured relations.

Complementary to this description are the paintings of the Sussex downlands by **Sir William Nicholson (1872-1949)**. Nicholson was fascinated by the great sweep of the downs and a series of paintings made between 1909 and 1914 are considered by many commentators to be some of his finest works. They have been described as "tonal" paintings and having an abstract, sleek, pared down appearance. Nicholson went on to paint similar views of the Wiltshire Downs in the 1920s following a move to Sutton Veny near Warminster in 1923.

Chalk downland landscape near Southerham
A deep chalk coombe in the South downs near Southerham, East Sussex. The chalk grassland has a rich flora including various orchids such as pyramidal orchid (foreground) and the rare burnt orchid (inset). The latter is a plant of short calcareous grassland and it usually has a preference for sunny, south-facing slopes. It occurs throughout England but the Wiltshire downs are its stronghold. It has undergone a drastic decline in numbers over the last hundred years such that it is now classed as endangered in Europe.

John Davis

Great Orme, North Wales

The limestone headland of the Great Orme (Pen-y-Gogarth) in North Wales supports species-rich calcareous grassland that contains a number of rare plants such as spotted cats-ear (Welsh name: Melynydd Brych) and spiked speedwell (Rhwyddlwyn Pigfain). The yellow-flowered hoary rockrose (Cor-rosyn Lledlwyd) is abundant in the grassland and the taller creamy-white flower spikes of dropwort (Crogedyf) are prominent. Male and female silver-studded blue butterflies (Gloyn Glas serennog) flit over the rocky pasture. This butterfly is patchily distributed across Great Britain and occurs primarily in limestone grassland and heathland. It is a declining species that disappeared from around 80% of its former range in the 20th century. The larvae feed on plants in the pea, heather and rock-rose families, particularly common and hoary rockrose, bird's-foot trefoil and ling. Throughout their development, the larva and pupa have an intimate relationship with two species of common black ants (*Lasius niger* and *L. alienus*). The larva produces sugar-rich liquid on which the ants feed and the ants provide the larva and pupa with protection from predators and parasites. Choughs (Brân goesgoch) are seen regularly from the Great Orme.

THE GREAT ORME, North Wales; John Davis

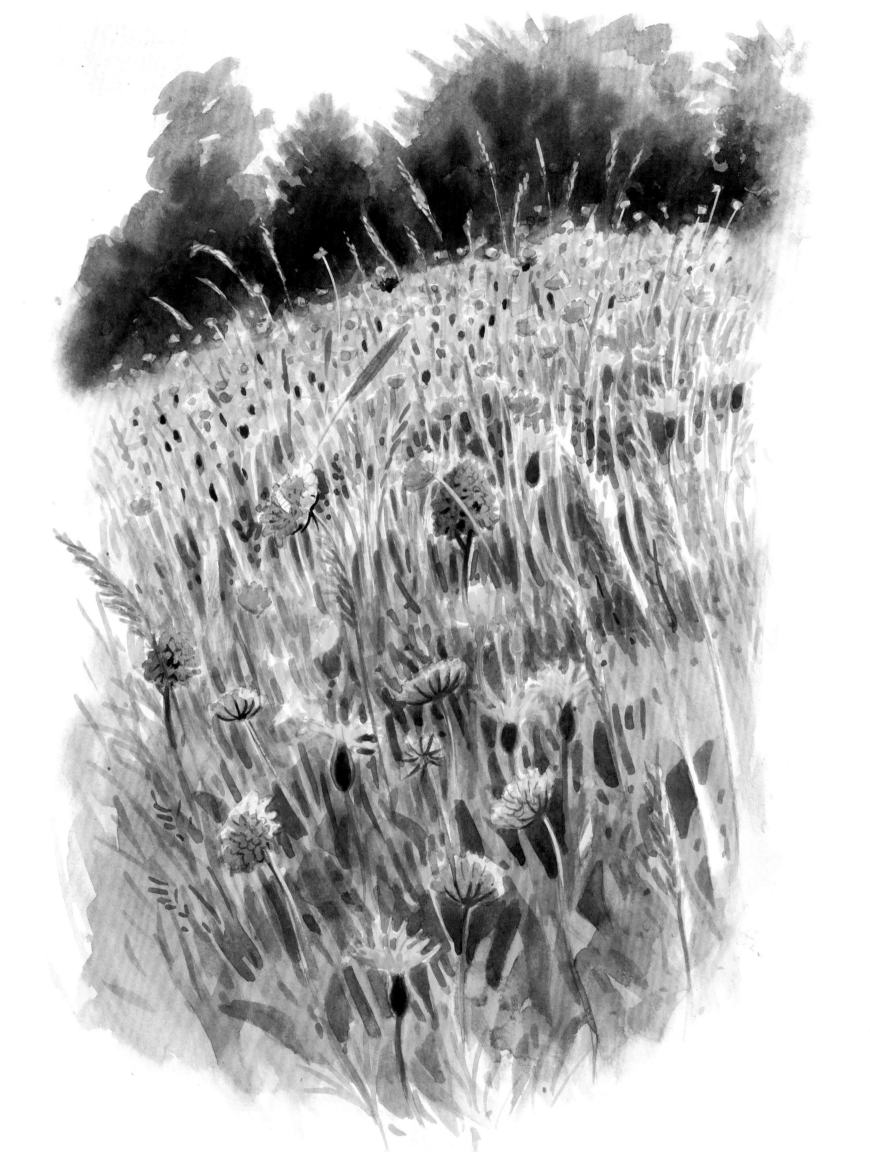

Bee orchid
An attractive orchid that has a preference for open or short grassland over chalk and limestone bedrock. It is widespread although rather local in England, but very rare in Scotland and largely confined to limestone grassland in the coastal zones of north and south Wales.

Opposite
Flowery chalk downland sward
A flowery chalk downland sward in July with rough hawkbit (yellow), small scabious (mauve), pyramidal orchid (dark pink) and upright brome grass.

Calcareous grassland occurs on shallow, infertile lime-rich soils over chalk and limestone bedrock or calcium-rich volcanic or metamorphic[1] rocks throughout Britain.

In lowland areas, many are now confined to steep valley slopes, escarpments, and coastal cliffs and headlands. More rarely they may occur on level ground such as in the East Anglian Breckland and Salisbury Plain.

These grasslands are typically unproductive, and are most suitable for low-intensity livestock grazing which is necessary for maintenance of the wildlife interest.

[1] A type of rock altered from its original state by pressure and heat

Kingley Vale and tumuli
Calcareous grassland with abundant devil's-bit scabious at Kingley Vale, West Sussex. The mounds are tumuli or burial mounds. The kestrel (flying over) is a common bird of downland as this habitat supports high densities of voles – the bird's favourite prey.

8th September 08 John Davis

Devil's-bit Scabious, Tumulus, Kingley Vale, West Sussex

Ox Pastures, Conistone Old Pastures
Ox Pastures (Conistone Old Pasture), Yorkshire Dales. Common wild thyme and birds-foot trefoil impart a mix of yellow and purple hues to this area of limestone grassland.

Conistone Old Pasture
Conistone Old Pasture is an extensive area of limestone grassland in the Yorkshire Dales. The pasture is like a yellow tapestry formed by the flowers of common rock rose. These flower-rich pastures are maintained by livestock grazing.

Conistone old Pasture:
with dense rock rose and birds foot trefoil:

John Davis
24 June·09

Moss campion
Moss campion is a cushion-forming plant of montane calcareous grasslands.

A significant amount of the lowland type of the habitat is found in England (90%), particularly on the chalk. In northern England and Scotland, the grassland often can be found in unenclosed situations in hill and mountain areas. Calcareous grasslands have a very rich flora of plants favouring lime-rich soils, including a number of orchids, some of which are rather rare. As many as 40 plant species can occur in a square metre of turf. Widespread plants include common rock rose (*Helianthemum nummularium*), salad burnet (*Sanguisorba minor*), small scabious (*Scabiosa columbaria*), wild thyme (*Thymus praecox*), fairy flax (*Linum catharticum*), harebell (*Campanula rotundifolia*) and the grasses sheep's fescue (*Festuca ovina*), upright brome (*Bromopsis erecta*), meadow oat (*Helictotrichon pratense*), quaking grass and crested hair grass (*Koeleria macrantha*).

Ox eye daisies, swifts and skylark
A colourful grassland with abundant ox-eye daisies and kidney vetch. Swifts scream overhead and a solitary skylark rises upwards.

11 June '08

Cowslips on the bank

Old Winchester Hill – cowslips on hill fort
Cowslips on the banks of the Iron Age hill fort at Old Winchester Hill
National Nature Reserve, Hampshire. This nature reserve was established to
conserve nationally important flower-rich calcareous grassland including a
large population of the local round-headed rampion. The site also supports
a large colony of juniper, a declining shrub for which there is a published
conservation action plan.

the hill fort at Old Winchester Hill - Hampshire

Rodborough Common, Gloucestershire
Rodborough Common in the Gloucestershire Cotswolds showing the
terraced limestone grassland slopes in summer. The sward, which is
dominated by tor grass and upright brome, (prominent in the foreground)
is rich in wildflowers, including a variety of orchids and herbs such
as common rock rose and the threatened pasque flower.

Barlavington Downs
A spectacular orchid display in June in chalk
grassland at Barlavington Downs, West Sussex.

John Davis

Linnets Barlaventon Down 1 June '08

26th July '08 Cissn Down, Sussex.

Grasses and marbled white butterfly
A selection of native grasses including quaking grass, crested dog's-tail and sweet vernal grass. A marbled white butterfly roosts on a grass stem.

Above right
Marbled white butterflies
This distinctive black and white butterfly is associated with semi-natural grasslands but it is especially abundant on calcareous grasslands in southern England. The caterpillars feed on various grasses including red fescue. The adult butterflies favour the purple and mauve flowers of members of the daisy and teasel families. Marbled white has shown an increase in abundance since the late1980s.

Opposite
Levin Down, West Sussex
This July scene shows the chalk grassland at Levin Down, West Sussex in its full glory with marjoram, clustered bellflower and round-headed rampion all in full flower. Two chalk hill blue butterflies feed on marjoram flowers. This species is characteristic of southern chalk grassland where the larvae feed on horsehoe vetch.

In northern England and central Scotland blue moor-grass (*Sesleria albicans*) is prominent in calcareous pastures in both lowland and upland areas. The higher altitude or more northerly calcareous grasslands, such as those found in Scotland, occur in a cool wet climate and have soils which are less lime-rich due to the removal of calcium from the root zone to lower levels in the soil through water percolation. Thus species typical of more neutral or mildly acidic soils are more common and include species such as common bent, sweet vernal grass, tormentil (*Potentilla erecta*) and heath bedstraw (*Galium saxatile*). In Scotland, in particular, high altitude calcareous grasslands are important for their montane flora, e.g. mountain avens (*Dryas octapetala*), moss campion (*Silene acaulis*) and alpine lady's mantle (*Alchemilla alpina*).

Flowery calcareous grassland sward
Calcareous grassland showing a myriad of flowering plants. The tall grass is mostly upright brome and the delicate drooping flowers of quaking grass can be seen in the right hand foreground. The pink spikes of pyramidal orchid are distinctive and there are drifts of white-flowered ox-eye daisies upslope. House martins and a hobby fly overhead.

John Laver

Martin Down, Hampshire
Martin Down National Nature Reserve comprises a large area of flower-rich chalk grassland in Hampshire. In this autumn view, the anthills formed by yellow meadow ant are prominent. Green woodpecker, here seen flying, will feed on the anthills.

Brown hare amongst red clover
Brown hare. This familiar mammal has a preference for open farmland with a mixture of arable, grassland pastures, hedgerows and small copses. During the day brown hares lie up in shallow depressions known as forms to avoid detection by predators. They occur throughout Great Britain except for parts of the highlands of Scotland. Numbers of brown hares appear to have remained stable over the last 15 to 20 years.

Brown hare study

fly orchid on scrub edge

Fly orchid
This is a species of calcareous grassland and scrub and woodland margins. It is now fairly scarce, having undergone a large decline over the last hundred years.

Early purple orchids and cowslips
The early purple orchid is one of several so-called ancient woodland species that also occur regularly in old pastures. This orchid is especially associated with calcareous grasslands. It has a wide variety of local names, including Goosey ganders and Adder's meat, suggesting that it was once very widespread and abundant.

John Davis

Early Purple Orchid + Cowslips
April · 09

Limestone pavement, Southerscales

Limestone pavement, Southerscales
Limestone pavement and grassland at Southerscales,
Yorkshire Dales with Ingleborough in the background.
A northern wheatear is perched on a limestone boulder.

Wheatears
The northern wheatear, a summer visitor to Great
Britain, breeds primarily in open moorland habitats
including semi-natural grasslands. The name wheatear
derives from two Old English words, hwit, 'white',
and aers, 'rump' or 'backside'. It was probably
changed to ear when arse acquired its vulgar
connotations in the 17th century.

Harting Down, West Sussex
Harting Down, West Sussex is of national importance for its flower-rich chalk grassland. The site supports several species of orchid, including common spotted orchid which is abundant along the edge of the track.

late Summer on Beeding hill, Sussex '09

Chalk grassland, Beeding Hill, Sussex

Flower-rich chalk grassland at Beeding Hill, West Sussex in late summer. The purple-flowered devil's-bit scabious is abundant in the sward and the adonis blue butterfly is on the wing. This butterfly is characteristic of southern chalk grassland where the turf is short. The larvae feed on horseshoe vetch. The male has brilliant blue wings but the females are brown. After a long period of decline this species has recently increased in abundance in some areas.

Clouded yellow

The clouded yellow butterfly is a migratory species which is a regular visitor to Great Britain. Arrivals will breed and the female lays her eggs on the leaves of legumes including clovers and bird's-foot trefoil. The clouded yellow seems to have a preference for calcareous grassland in southern England.

Grayling

The grayling butterfly now has a decidedly coastal distribution in Great Britain but still occurs on inland calcareous grasslands, especially in southern England. It also occurs on acid grassland and heathland, for example in the Breckland of East Anglia. The caterpillars feed on a variety of grasses.

Cowslips in the snow
Cowslips in the snow at Bepton Down,
West Sussex in early April.

84

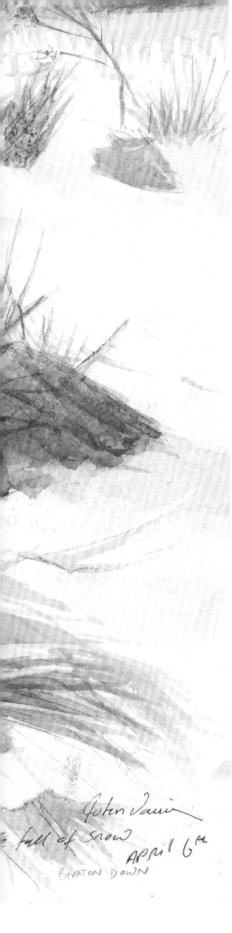

John Davin

fall of snow
APRIL 6th
BEATON DOWN

Fox and fieldfares, Harting Down
Harting Down, West Sussex. A fox traverses the chalk downland
slope whilst a flock of fieldfares can be seen overhead.

From downland
to upland

Downland cowslips
Cowslips on chalk
downland at Kithurst
Hill, West Sussex.

Mountain avens
Mountain avens is a typical mat-forming
plant of upland calcareous grasslands. The
picture shows the exquisite white flowers
and the twisted feathery seed-heads.

Alpine lady's-mantle and alpine club moss
Alpine lady's mantle and alpine club moss. Both these species
are associated with upland calcareous and acid grasslands or grass-
heaths, the former species occurring in Scotland and Cumbria,
the latter in Wales, northern England and Scotland.

87

Common spotted orchids
Common spotted orchids in chalk grassland in June.

Spotted orchids, June.08

John Davis

Pasque flower
Pasque flower is a very showy plant that is entirely restricted to lowland calcareous grasslands in England. It is now known from only 18 sites in central and eastern England. It flowers around Eastertime (mid-April) – the name 'pasque' meaning like 'paschal' – of Easter. John Clare, the poet, found it near the village of Helpston in Northamptonshire.

Dark red helleborine
Dark red helleborine is a scarce orchid characteristic of limestone grasslands, pavements and cliff ledges in northern England and north Wales. It also occurs sporadically in east-central, north and north-west Scotland.

Calcareous grasslands are particularly important as habitats for threatened plants; examples for lowland areas include various orchids such as burnt orchid (*Orchis ustulata*), late spider orchid (*Ophrys fuciflora*) and man orchid (*Aceras anthropophorum*), purple milk-vetch (*Astragalus danicus*), pasque flower (*Pulsatilla vulgaris*) and white rock-rose (*Helianthemum apenninum*). The rather local orchid, dark red helleborine (*Epipactis atrorubens*), is a feature of some northern and upland calcareous grasslands, and in higher altitude grasslands, the rare Sibbaldia (*Sibbaldia procumbens*), a type of cinquefoil belonging to the rose family, may be found.

Frizzled crisp-moss
(tortella tortuosa)

Calcareous grassland mosses
Two calcareous grassland mosses;
comb-moss (*Ctenidium molluscum*)
and frizzled crisp-moss (*Tortella
tortuosa*).

Comb Moss (Ctenidium Molluscum)

Calcareous grassland, especially where the turf is short and there is plenty of bare ground, can also be significant for mosses, liverworts and lichens.

It can support either a rich assemblage of more common species and/or a range of scarcer ones.

Typical widespread species include yellow feather-moss (*Homalothecium lutescens*) and comb-moss (*Ctenidium molluscum*), *Cladonia rangiformis* (a lichen) and, in upland or northern sites, frizzled crisp-moss (*Tortella tortuosa*).

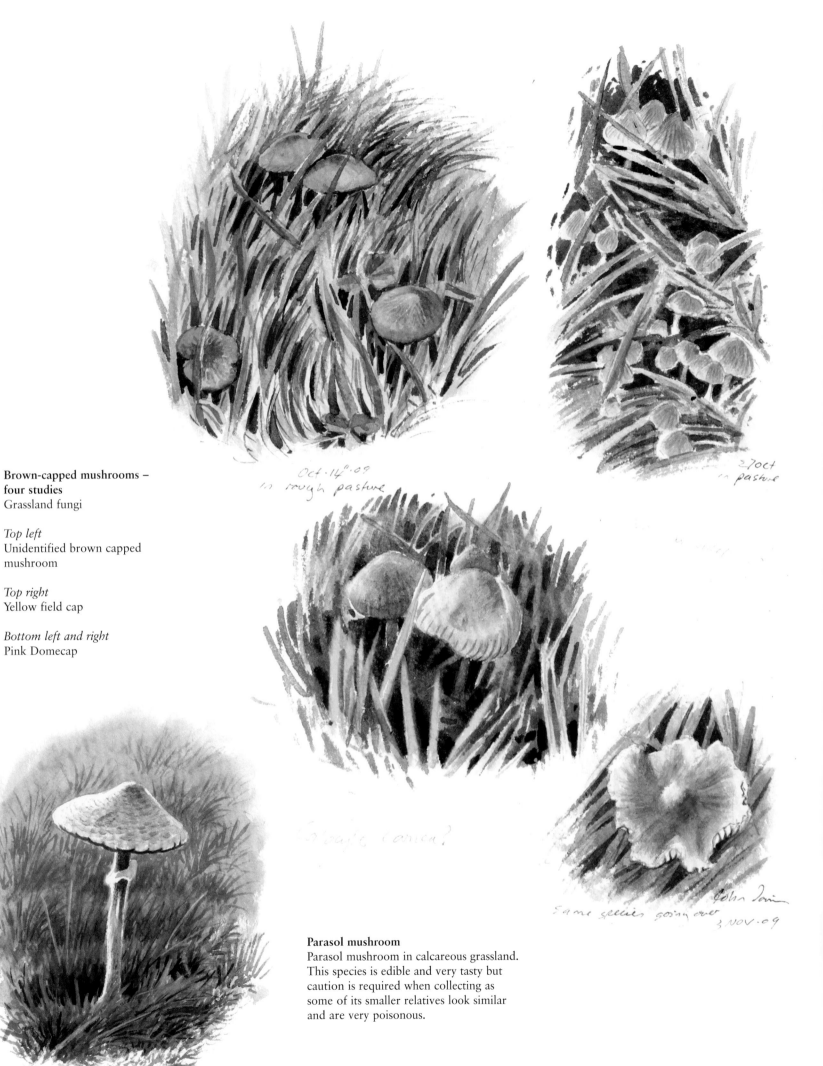

**Brown-capped mushrooms –
four studies**
Grassland fungi

Top left
Unidentified brown capped
mushroom

Top right
Yellow field cap

Bottom left and right
Pink Domecap

Oct.14⁰.09
in rough pasture

27oct
in pasture

same species going over
3 NOV.09

Parasol mushroom
Parasol mushroom in calcareous grassland.
This species is edible and very tasty but
caution is required when collecting as
some of its smaller relatives look similar
and are very poisonous.

Grassland fungi
Wildflower-rich grasslands can be important habitats for various species of fungi, notably waxcaps.

From left to right, top to bottom
Orange mosscap (*Rickenella fibula*), Fairy ring champignons[1] (*Marismius oreades*), a grassland mushroom (unidentified), Pleated inkcap (*Coprinus plicatilis*), Mower's mushroom or Brown mottlegill (*Panaeolina foenisecii*), Yellow fieldcap (*Bolbitius vitellinus*), Waxcaps (*Hygrocybe spp*) in chalk grassland.

[1] Fairy rings, also known as elf circles or pixie rings, consist of a circle of mushrooms, that often cause the grass to turn darker green. They actually result from the growth of various fungi (mushrooms and toadstools). Underneath the ring in the soil, there is a mass of branching thread-like hyphae (long branching filamentous cells of a fungus) which is the vegetative part of the fungi. There are a number of species of grassland fungi that form fairy rings; one of the best known is the fairy ring champignon. Many superstitious beliefs have developed over time to explain the phenomenon, starting in the Middle Ages. Further detailed explanation of fairy rings can found in the excellent book on Fungi by Brian Spooner and Peter Roberts in the Collins New Naturalist Library (Number 96).

Oystercatcher and melancholy thistle
Oystercatcher is an unmistakeable wader that now
regularly breeds in a variety of upland habitats such
as occur in the northern Pennines. Melancholy thistle
is a plant that is typical of flower-rich upland hay
meadows and roadside verges in the north Pennines
and Cumbria. It can also be found in open woods,
limestone pavements and on cliff ledges.

Melancholy Thistle   June·09

Young wheatears on downland
Wheatears, once a characteristic breeding species of southern chalk downland, now rarely breed in this habitat but may sometimes be seen on migration.

Young Wheatear on Downland 1 oct. 09

Cock wheatear and violets
A cock wheatear in chalk downland in spring.

Badgers and fallow deer
Badgers at a sett on chalk
downland near Kingley Vale.
A fallow deer grazes in the
background.

Badger on downland
A badger forages for earthworms in the short chalk
downland turf following emergence from a sett at dusk.

Fauna – lowland

Lowland calcareous grassland provides an
important habitat for birds. Species such as
skylark and meadow pipit, whilst still declining,
remain relatively widespread. The chalk
grasslands of the East Anglian Breckland and
the Wiltshire Downs are strongholds for the
rare stone curlew (*Burhinus oedicnemus*),
currently numbering around 350 breeding pairs.
This species is a spring summer visitor to Britain
and nests on sparsely vegetated and bare stony
ground, feeding on earthworms, woodlice
and beetles.

Stone curlew, lapwings and rabbit
At Weeting Heath in Breckland, the short-turf maintained by rabbits is an ideal habitat for breeding stone curlew and lapwing. The stone curlew is a rare spring and summer visitor to England with around 350 breeding pairs. It is associated with tightly grazed or sparsely vegetated chalk and acid grassland and with spring-sown arable crops.

Stone curlew study
Stone curlews at Weeting Heath, Norfolk.

Chalk and limestone grasslands support a tremendous variety of insects and other invertebrates. For example, for butterflies, the richest and most important farmland habitat is semi-natural grassland pasture, especially chalk and limestone grassland. These pastures provide a breeding habitat for nearly 90% of British species (48 of the 55), including widespread species such as common blue (*Polyommatus icarus*) and marbled white (*Melanargia galathea*). Twenty butterflies are closely associated with chalk and limestone grassland, including threatened species such as small blue (*Cupido minimus*), northern brown argus (*Aricia artaxerxes*) and Duke of Burgundy (*Hamearis lucina*).

Small blue butterfly
Small blue butterfly on a kidney vetch flower. The latter is also the larval food plant. Small blue is the smallest British resident butterfly and is characteristic of calcareous grassland, especially in southern England.

Chalk carpet moth
Chalk carpet moth on bird's foot trefoil. The moth is nocturnal but it is readily disturbed during the daytime and flies short distances before re-settling.

Chalk hill blue butterflies, Levin Down
Chalk hill blue butterflies, Levin Down, West Sussex. The chalk grassland has an abundance of pink-flowered marjoram and, in the foreground, the deep purple-flowered clustered bellflower.

Six-spot burnet moths
Six spot burnet moths on the flowers of round-headed rampion and small scabious. The moths fly on sunny days in July and August.

Hundreds of Six-spot Burnet moths on Round-headed RAMPIONS and Scabious   8 July·09

John Davis

Grizzled skippers
The grizzled skipper is a characteristic early-flying butterfly of chalk downland in southern England. The caterpillars feed on a variety of plants including common agrimony and wild strawberry. Here the butterfly is settled on the flowers of sweet vernal grass.

Grizzled skipper
on Sweet vernal grass

June 15th. 09
Cerin Down

Grizzled &
Dingy skippers together.

Duke of Burgundy: May '09

Cowslips and Duke of Burgundy butterfly
The Duke of Burgundy butterfly is typical of woodland rides and glades and scrubby calcareous grassland where the caterpillars feed on cowslips and primroses. It occurs in scattered, small colonies mostly in southern England but with a few populations in North Yorkshire and Lancashire.

Brown argus and marjoram
Brown argus butterfly on a marjoram flower on chalk downland in late summer. The bell-shaped flowers of harebell and the mauve, flat-topped flowers of small scabious are also present in the herbage. Brown argus is a characteristic of southern calcareous grassland where the caterpillars feed on common rock rose.

Calcareous grasslands also support a wide diversity of moths including the day-flying five-spot and six-spot burnet moths (*Zygaena trifollii*, downland race, and *Z. filipendulae*) and the cistus forester (*Adscita geryon*), the larval foodplants being bird's foot-trefoil (for both burnet moths) and common rock-rose respectively. The chalk carpet (*Scotopteryx bipunctaria*), a rather uncommon moth, likes short-grazed calcareous grassland with plenty of bare ground. The larvae feed on various legumes including bird's-foot trefoil. It is widespread in southern and central England and along the coastline of Wales and northern England and southern Scotland.

Opposite
Roman snail, moss and lichen
The Roman snail was introduced into
Great Britain by the Romans for
gastronomic reasons! It occurs in
calcareous grassland and woodland in
southern England. It is generally active
between May and August but hibernates
in winter. It is the largest snail in Great
Britain and is now endangered across its
European range.

Stripe-winged grasshopper

Such grassland is also a rich
habitat for grasshoppers and
crickets, including two uncommon
calcareous grassland specialists,
rufous grasshopper (*Gomphocerippus
rufus*) and stripe-winged grasshopper
(*Stenobothrus lineatus*), both confined
to southern and eastern England.

Rufous grasshopper

The glow worm (*Lampyris noctiluca*) is closely
associated with chalk and limestone grassland.
It is actually a type of beetle, and it is the wingless
female that emits a pale yellowish-green light,
usually between between 10 and 11p.m. on
summer evenings! It is widespread but local,
with a southern bias.

Short-grazed calcareous grassland can support an
assemblage of snails, including widespread species
such as the striped snail (*Cernuella virgata*) and
the wrinkled snail (*Candidula intersecta*). The rare
Carthusian snail (*Monacha cartusiana*) is
restricted to calcareous grassland largely in south
east England.

A prominent feature of calcareous grasslands in the lowlands are the anthills constructed by the yellow meadow ant (*Lasius flavus*). These can be of substantial size, the largest being up to 50 centimetres high with a volume of up to 200 litres. The tops of the anthills have a distinctive flora, with species such as wild thyme, common rockrose, thyme-leaved sandwort (*Arenaria serpyllifolia*), wall speedwell (*Veronica arvensis*), and common mouse-ear chickweed (*Cerastium fontanum*) being especially common. The distinctive rose-moss (*Rhodobryum roseum*) is a rather scarce species that has a preference for anthills.

Anthills and wild thyme
Anthills carpeted in wild thyme on Harting Downs, West Sussex. The grass protruding from the centre rear of the larger anthill is crested hair grass, a specialist species of dry calcareous grassland.

Green woodpecker on anthill
A male green woodpecker feeds at an anthill. Ants and their eggs and larvae form an important component of the diet of green woodpeckers.

Anthill
Moss-covered anthill on chalk downland with harebell, rough hawkbit and wild basil in the foreground.

John Nash

Moss-covered Ant-hill
with hare-bell + wild basil
Sept. 09

ROCK ROSE, Levin Down Sussex

Common rockrose
Common rockrose on Levin Down, West Sussex. This perennial shrubby species is typical of ancient calcareous grassland in Great Britain.

Northern brown argus and rock rose
The northern brown argus butterfly occurs in mostly small colonies on northern calcareous (limestone) grasslands in the far north of England and in Scotland. Other than a stronghold in Dumfries and Galloway, its Scottish distribution is primarily eastern with the most northerly sites being in Easter Ross. The larvae feed on common rock rose. It is on the wing from mid-June until early August.

Black grouse
Black grouse is a striking game bird here pictured in meadows and pastures in Upper Teesdale, County Durham in June. The species has been declining across Europe and in Great Britain. It is now largely restricted to the northern Pennines, north Wales and Scotland. Black grouse seem to prefer landscapes with a mosaic of habitats including moorland or heathland, grassland, mires and scattered trees and shrubs. The 'blackcocks' form leks (communal gatherings of displaying male birds) on spring mornings on semi-natural grasslands or mires. The lek is designed to attract females and blackcocks which achieve central locations get the most opportunities to mate with the hen birds. This bird has recently been the focus for conservation recovery and management programmes (see British Wildlife article by Phil Warren 2010).

Fauna – upland

Calcareous grasslands in the uplands above the moor wall may support a range of typical moorland birds such as skylark, meadow pipit, wheatear (*Oenanthe oenanthe*), lapwing and golden plover (*Pluvialis apricaria*), which breed or feed there. The invertebrate fauna is not as rich as that associated with lowland calcareous grassland, but nonetheless there are a number of rare species associated with the habitat. These include a mason bee (*Osmia parietina*) and the upland pill woodlouse (*Armadillidium pictum*). The former has a close association with bird's-foot trefoil which is the bee's main source of pollen.

Acid grasslands

Although perhaps not as immediately visually striking as old meadows or chalk downland, Britain's acid grasslands do nonetheless have their own unique appeal. In early summer, for example, the drier types of acid grasslands typical of lowland Britain such as in the East Anglian Breckland and the Lincolnshire Coversands, can be a tapestry of colours woven from the flowers of small plants such as mouse-ear hawkweed, biting stonecrop and common stork's-bill. Brightly-coloured waxcap fungi, so-named because of their shiny, waxy caps, are a conspicuous feature of some acid grasslands.

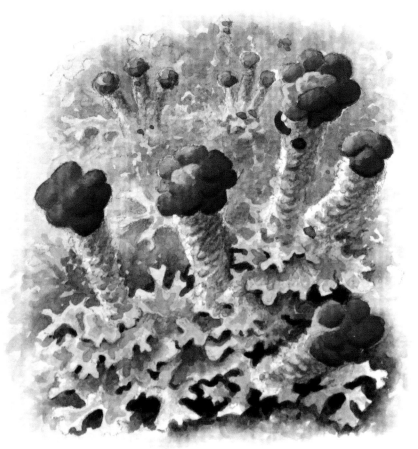

A Cladonia lichen
A species of "reindeer lichen" (*Cladonia* spp) showing the red fruiting bodies.

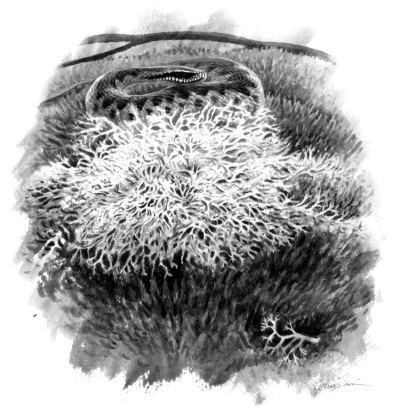

Cladonia lichen, moss and adder
Acid grassland with Bog groove-moss (*Aulaconmium palustre*) (foreground) , a "reindeer lichen", (*Cladonia portentosa*) (middle distance) and adder. The adder or viper occurs in a variety of habitats and has a widespread but patchy distribution in Great Britain. Heathlands, acid grasslands, moors, dunes, chalk grassland and woodland rides are particularly favoured.

Acid grasslands occur on infertile acid soils developed over sandstones, acid igneous rocks, or sands and gravels in the lowlands and upland fringes. Often associated with lowland dwarf shrub heath – in a wide variety of landscape situations, ranging from level plains such as in the East Anglian Breckland to steep valley slopes – these grasslands are typically unproductive and are thus most suitable for low-intensity livestock grazing.

The fine-leaved grasses common bent and sheep's fescue are almost always present. Typical herbs include sheep's sorrel (*Rumex acetosella*), tormentil and heath bedstraw. Lichens can be a prominent feature of some drier acid grasslands, particularly species of *Cladonia*.

Tormentil
Tormentil is associated with
many types of flower-rich
grassland but is most prevalent
where the soils are moderately
to strongly acidic.

Tormentil   19 Jly·09

John Davis

Grassland fungi
Top: Fungi on a moss-covered ant hill, Petworth Park, West Sussex. These agaric mushrooms are probably a species of pinkgill in the genus *Entoloma*
Bottom: Snowy wax cap (*Hygrocybe virginea*), Petworth Park

Blackening waxcap
Blackening waxcap (*Hygrocybe conica*).

Threatened plant species associated with acid grassland include maiden pink (*Dianthus deltoides*) and smooth cat's ear (*Hypochaeris glabra*).

Fungi such as wax-caps, earth-tongues and fairy clubs can be abundant, particularly in western Britain.

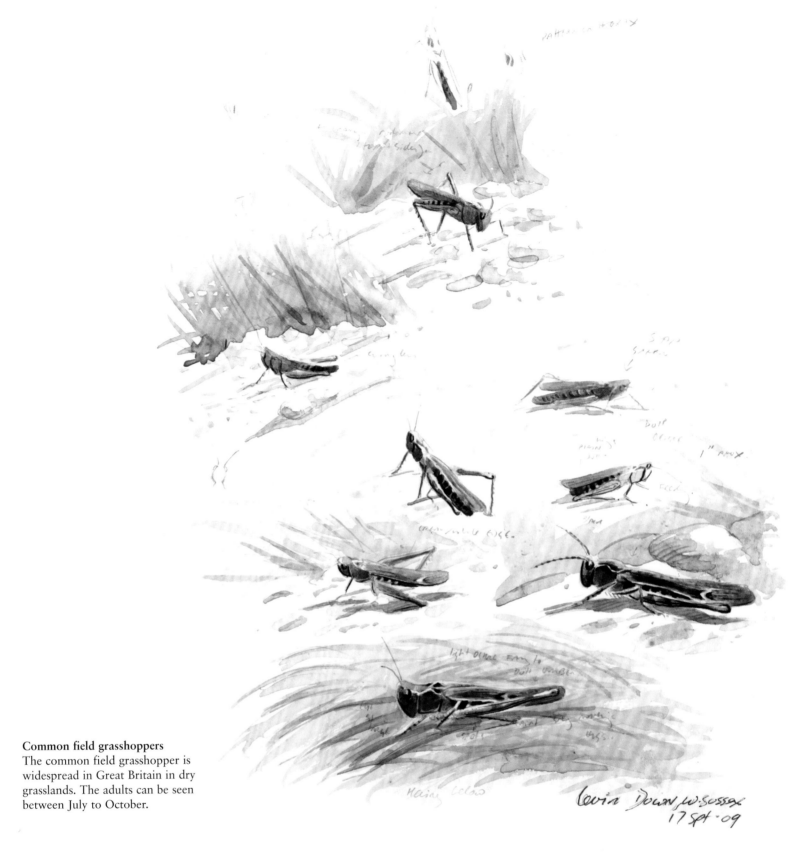

Common field grasshoppers
The common field grasshopper is widespread in Great Britain in dry grasslands. The adults can be seen between July to October.

Acid grassland also provides a habitat for a variety of birds, reptiles and invertebrates. Lapwing, skylark, meadow pipit and, at some sites in eastern and southern England, woodlark (*Lullula arborea*) may occur. Snakes and lizards such as adder (*Vipera berus*) and common lizard (*Zootoca vivipara*) may also be found associated with acid grassland. The open parched acid grasslands on light sandy soils in particular can support a considerable number of ground-dwelling and burrowing invertebrates such as solitary bees and wasps. Butterflies such as the common blue, small copper and small heath are widespread, and more locally the silver-studded blue (*Plebejus argus*) and grayling (*Hipparchia semele*) may occur. These latter two butterflies are both threatened species.

Curlew on drystone wall
A curlew on a drystone wall at Conistone Old Pasture,
Yorkshire Dales. Robbie Burns (1759-1796), Scotland's best-
loved bard, wrote that he had 'never heard the loud solitary
whistle of a curlew on a summer noon... without feeling
an elevation of the soul'.

John Davis

Curlew at Conistone old pasture.

Southern marsh-orchids
Southern marsh-orchids. This orchid occurs
in central and southern England and southern
Wales in lowland regions. It is a plant of marshy
grassland with a preference for sites with
alkaline soils.

Marshy grasslands

**To the casual observer, these marshy pastures
may appear rather dull and drab when seen from
a distance. However, in mid-summer, the visitor
may experience fine displays of various species
of purple or pink-flowered orchids, and the
prominent yellow flowers of tormentil and greater
bird's foot trefoil. Later in the summer, the purple
flowers of devil's-bit scabious and the burnt
yellow flower spikes of bog asphodel may be
evident. On calm, sunny days in summer,
dragonflies and damselflies may be seen darting
and fluttering around as they hunt for insect prey.**

The marshy grasslands, sometimes known
as purple moor-grass and rush pastures, are
dominated by purple moor-grass (*Molinia
caerulea*) and/or jointed rushes (*Juncus* spp)
and are usually managed as cattle pasture or
more rarely as hay meadows. These pastures
occur mostly on gently sloping ground associated
with springs and spring lines but also on level
ground adjacent to rivers and lakes. They are
found on infertile poorly-draining, neutral or
mildly acidic peaty mineral soils. These marshy
pastures are generally more widespread in
western areas of Britain, particularly in Wales
and south-west England.

This habitat supports a wide range of flowers
characteristic of periodically wet conditions.
These include cuckoo flower (*Cardamine
pratensis*), meadowsweet, ragged robin (*Lychnis
flos-cuculi*), tormentil, devil's-bit scabious (*Succisa
pratensis*), common marsh-bedstraw (*Galium
palustre*) and greater bird's-foot trefoil (*Lotus
pedunculatus*). Marshy grasslands often have an
abundance of small sedges (*Carex spp*) and the
richest type occurs on soils that are slightly limey.
In southern Britain, these may support
populations of meadow thistle.

Threatened plants characteristic of these
grasslands include whorled caraway (*Carum
verticillatum*) and Cambridge milk-parsley
(*Selinum carvifolia*), members of the carrot family
(Umbelliferae) and heath lobelia (*Lobelia urens*).

119

Pocklington Canal and Melbourne Ings
Fen meadows adjacent to the Pocklington
Canal, East Yorkshire. These wet meadows,
known locally as Ings, have a rich flora
including species such as marsh marigold,
sneezewort, early marsh orchid, bog bean
and the threatened marsh pea. The Ings also
support important breeding populations of
waders such as curlew and snipe.

Pocklington Canal   24 June 09   John Davis

Marshy grassland, West Sussex
Marshy grassland in West Sussex with
devil's-bit scabious and tormentil. Two
roe deer look on in the background.

Meadow pipit

Meadow pipit amongst rough hawkbit, a member of the daisy family. Meadow pipit is a very common species that breeds in a wide range of habitats including flower-rich grasslands in Great Britain. It feeds mostly on invertebrates including flies, beetles and moth larvae but, in autumn and winter, it will eat the seeds of various plants including grasses.

meadow pipit and Hawkbit
Sept 09
John Davis

Curlews feeding in rough pasture

Curlews feeding in rough pasture, near Pagham, North Wall, West Sussex.

123

Lapwing in a Perthshire pasture
Lapwing on a nest in a Perthshire marshy grassland pasture. The
sitting bird is surrounded by the pink blooms of cuckoo flower.

A varied insect fauna can be found in this habitat.
One of the best known insects is the uncommon
marsh fritillary butterfly (*Euphydryas aurinia*),
which occurs on these wet pastures in western
Britain. Its larval food plant is devil's-bit scabious.
The young caterpillars live colonially within a
silken web draped over the leaves of the food
plant. Adult butterflies are on the wing in late
May and June. The marsh fritillary thrives under
a regime of low-density cattle grazing which
maintains a varied range of vegetation heights and
promotes devil's-bit scabious to produce larger
plants. These are more suitable for larval
development. Another special insect to be found
is the day-flying narrow-bordered bee hawk-
moth. The moth mimics the appearance of a
bumblebee and it can be seen on the wing in May
and June visiting various flowers. The larval food
plant is also devil's-bit scabious.

Marshy grasslands may provide breeding areas for
wading birds such as curlew, lapwing and snipe.

Lapwing chicks
Lapwing chicks in rushy pasture.

Marsh fritillary

Marsh fritillary butterfly on devil's-bit scabious, the main larval food plant. This combination is for illustrative purposes as the flight period of the butterfly does not normally coincide with the larval food plant in flower.

Curlew in marshy grassland

Curlew in marshy grassland. The sitting bird is surrounded by the pink flowers of ragged robin, the silky white seed heads of common cotton grass and the spikes of soft rush. Curlew breeds in a wide variety of habitats including grazing marshes, flood meadows, marshy grassland, moorland, bogs and lowland heaths. One estimate is that there are at least 97, 000 breeding pairs in Great Britain.

Cuckoo flower and orange tip butterfly
Cuckoo flower, or lady's smock, is a plant of damp meadows and pastures. It is the main food plant of the caterpillars of the orange tip butterfly. This butterfly is on the wing in spring, usually between mid-April and mid-June.

Studies at Balranald N.Uist 22 may   *John Davis*

Scottish machair

Lapwings, Balranald, North Uist
Lapwing and chicks amongst the damper grasslands of the North Uist machair.

Machair landscape
Machair grassland at Balranald, North Uist, Outer Hebrides. The machair is an important breeding and feeding habitat for several waders including redshank (Gaelic: Maor-cladaich) (on nearest post), dunlin and lapwing (Curracag). In the foreground, a corncrake (Traon) skulks in the taller vegetation whilst skylark (Uiseag), another species that commonly breeds on the machair, flies overhead.

Machair is scenically very special. The combination of sea, sweeping white-shell beaches, dunes and flower-rich machair grassland backed by marshy grassland and lochs often set against a backdrop of hills and mountains, is a visual treat. In spring and summer this delightful landscape is enriched by the calls of birds and a myriad of colourful wild flowers including orchids.

The word 'machair' is Gaelic, meaning an extensive, low-lying fertile plain. It has now become a recognised term for a distinctive type of grazed grassland occurring on flat areas behind sand dunes on coastal lime-rich sandy soils that are subject to periodic rotational arable cultivation for growing oats, rye and potatoes.

Ringed plovers

Ringed plovers (Trillachan-tràghad) on coastal grassland at Balranald, North Uist. Thrift or sea pink (Tonnachladaich), sea campion (Coirean na Mara) and daisy are prominent in the sward. Ringed plover is a characteristic breeding species of the machair grasslands.

John Davis

Balranald, on headland amongst thrift
+ sea campion and daisies.

22 May 2000

Dunlin on the machair
Dunlin (Gille-feadaig) breed on the
flowery Scottish machair grassland. This
sward is rich in daisies (Neòinan), meadow
buttercups (Buidheag an t-Samhraidh) and
ribwort plantain (Slàn-lus).

The machair system is typically a "low
input-output" farming system but with
some soil enrichment through the
application of seaweed as a fertiliser.

Machair has developed under wet and windy
oceanic conditions. However, the term is often
applied more widely to include the whole
"system" of offshore seabed, beach, dunes,
plain, and inland marshes and lochs.

This habitat is found only in the north and west
of Britain and Ireland. Almost half of the Scottish
machair occurs in the Outer Hebrides, with the
best and most extensive in the Uists and Barra,
and also on Tiree. Machair sand has a high shell
content, sometimes 80-90%.

Machair grassland has a very rich flora and fauna.
Red fescue, smooth meadow grass (*Poa pratensis*),
lady's bedstraw, white clover, yarrow (*Achillea
millefolium*), common bird's-foot trefoil, ribwort
plantain (*Plantago lanceolata*), daisy (*Bellis
perennis*), meadow buttercup, self heal (*Prunella
vulgaris*), and eyebrights (*Euphrasia* spp) all occur.

Golden plovers, North Uist
Although golden plover
(Feadag-bhuidhe) usually
breeds on bogs and peaty
areas, it does use the machair
on North Uist for feeding
both during and outside the
breeding season.

Corn bunting
Corn bunting is a bird of lowland farmland and prefers open landscapes of mixed pasture and arable land. It will nest in semi-natural grassland, especially chalk grassland. Adults mostly eat seeds whereas the chicks are fed mainly on invertebrates. This rather drab bird has a distinctive 'jangling of keys' type song.

A feature of the machair are the spectacular orchid displays. Hebridean common spotted orchid (*Dactylorhiza fuchsii subsp hebridensis*), in particular, can be very abundant with thousands of flowering spikes occurring in some areas. Other species include early marsh orchid (*Dactylorhiza incarnata subsp coccinea*), heath fragrant orchid (*Gymnadenia borealis*), frog orchid (*Coeloglossum viride*), twayblade (*Listera ovata*) and northern marsh orchid (*Dactylorhiza purpurella*). The Hebridean marsh orchid (*Dactylorhiza ebudensis*) is only known from the North Uist machair.

High densities of breeding waders such as lapwing, ringed plover, and dunlin, plus skylark and corn bunting breed on the machair. Hen harriers hunt overhead during the spring and summer. The belted beauty (a moth) (*Lycia zonaria*) can be abundant, with its larvae feeding on bird's-foot trefoil and clovers (*Trifolium* spp).

The machair is the stronghold for the corncrake in Great Britain where it uses machair meadow-land and other tall vegetation for breeding.

Bumble bees are common, including the great yellow bumble bee (*Bombus distinguendus*), a scarce and declining species for which the machair is a particular stronghold. The machair grasslands have abundant red clover (*Trifolium pratense*), the flowers of which are an essential food source for this bumble bee.

West Sedgemoor, Somerset Levels
Spring scene at West Sedgemoor on the Somerset Levels. The Levels have important concentrations of wildflower-rich damp meadows and rush pastures which, in turn, provide a breeding habitat for waders and wildfowl. The ditches or rhynes also have high wildlife value, supporting a range of aquatic invertebrates including scarce water beetles and dragonflies. They also are a habitat for locally rare plants such as flowering rush and frogbit.

Early spring at West Sedgemoor

Bewick's Swan study
Bewick's swans in winter on Amberley Wild Brooks, West Sussex.
This species of conservation concern is a winter visitor to Great
Britain. The birds that winter in Britain breed in the western
Siberian tundra during the summer.

Coastal and flood plain grazing marsh

Grazing marshes are one of our most valued low-lying landscapes. They are wide open expanses of pasture or meadow criss-crossed with gleaming ditches In river valleys, the ditches may be bordered with pollarded willows and fringed by luxuriant vegetation of reeds, sedges and speckled with colourful flowers such as yellow flag iris, purple loosestrife and flowering rush. In spring, they may resound to the cry of waders including the bubbling call of the curlew. In winter, when flooded, they may attract large flocks of wildfowl and waders when a characteristic sound is the whistling calls of flocks of wigeon.

Grazing marsh consists of flat, open, low-lying expanses of wet grassland, criss-crossed by ditches which serve as field boundaries. They may also contain seasonally-wet hollows, permanent ponds and smaller areas of swamp dominated by large sedges and grasses. The habitat occurs in inland river valleys and on the coast adjacent to sea walls. They are often flooded, or at least experience high water levels, during winter. The grassland is grazed or cut for hay or silage, with much of it having undergone some degree of agricultural improvement; thus it mostly comprises improved or semi-improved grassland.

Silver Y moths and Whinchat
The Silver Y moth is a common visitor to most parts of Great Britain from spring until late autumn. It flies by day and by night. The illustration shows the moths on the flowers of common knapweed at Barlavington Down.

Whinchat on barbed wire. This summer visitor to Great Britain uses a fence as a vantage point for looking for its insect prey.

Amberley Wild Brooks in winter
A winter scene at Amberley Wild Brooks. A female
hen harrier quarters over the flooded pastures and
a flock of lapwings can be seen overhead.

Amberley Wildbrooks Jan '98

Bewick's swans in flight
Bewick's swans returning to flooded pastures.

Winter Floods on the Ouse

John Davis

Amberley Wild brooks JAN·05

Amberley Wild brooks in winter with wigeon
A flock of wigeon grazing pasture in winter at Amberley Wild Brooks, West Sussex. In the foreground, three fieldfares look poised to fly off. Wigeon is one of the most numerous of Britain's wintering waterbirds. This herbivorous duck breeds from Iceland across Scandinavia and Russia from the arctic tundra as far south as the temperate steppe zones.

Some grazing marshes (e.g. Derwent Ings, Somerset Levels) however, still retain large areas of species-rich semi-natural grassland (see old meadows and pastures and marshy grassland descriptions). Grazing marshes support important populations of wintering birds such as Bewick's swan (*Cygnus bewickii*), whooper swan (*Cygnus cygnus*), wigeon (*Anas penelope*), teal (*Anas crecca*), bean goose (*Anser fabalis*), and golden plover and breeding birds such as snipe, lapwing, curlew, redshank, shoveler (*Anas clypeata*), yellow wagtail and the rare garganey (*Anas querquedula*).

Opposite
Wigeon and sheep
Mixed flock of wigeon feeding in pasture alongside sheep. The males have a distinctive chestnut head and neck and a creamy-yellow forehead and crown. A solitary curlew is feeding behind a ewe.

142

John Davis

Bewick's swans at Amberley
Bewick's swans in winter at Amberley Wild Brooks, West Sussex. This species
frequents flooded grasslands where it will feed on various pasture grasses.

Grazing marsh ditches can be rich in flowering plants and invertebrates. Of the former, widespread species include various submerged plants of open water such as water milfoils (*Myriophyllum* spp), pondweeds (*Potamogeton* spp), and water crowfoots (*Ranunculus* [sub-genus *Batrachium*] spp), plants with floating leaves such as water starworts (*Callitriche* spp), duckweeds (*Lemna* spp) and amphibious bistort (*Polygonum amphibium*), and emergent species rooted in the sediments such as yellow iris (*Iris pseudocorus*), water plantain (*Alisma plantago-aquaticum*), fool's water-cress (*Apium nodiflorum*), purple-loosestrife (*Lythrum salicaria*) and the more local flowering rush (*Butomus umbellatus*), plus large bulky grasses and "reed/rush-like plants" such as reed sweet grass

(*Glyceria maxima*), bulrush (*Typha latifolia*), common club-rush (*Schoenoplectus lacustris*) and bur-reeds (*Sparganium* spp). Threatened species such as the greater water-parsnip (*Sium latifolium*) and tubular water dropwort (*Oenanthe fistulosa*) can occur in ditches, especially in central and southern England. Brackish grassland may support scarce plants such as sea clover (*Trifolium squamosum*).

Ditches have a rich invertebrate fauna and, in particular, support important assemblages of dragonflies, damselflies (larvae), water beetles and snails. Two uncommon invertebrates of grazing marsh ditches are the hairy dragonfly (*Brachytron pratense*) and the great silver water beetle (*Hydrophilus piceus*).

144

Short-eared owl study
Short-eared owls are open country birds. In winter,
birds hunt over coastal and floodplain grazing
marshes, reedbeds, saltmarshes and chalk downland.

Amberley Wild Brooks in early summer
Amberley Wild Brooks, West Sussex is an extensive area of grazing marsh criss-crossed by ditches. The ditches have a rich flora including a number of uncommon species. The flowering spikes of yellow flag iris are conspicuous in the early summer. A hobby, a summer visitor to Great Britain, can be seen hunting dragonflies over the marsh.

Amberley Wildbrooks, may-09 John Davis

Redshank on a post, Avon Valley

Redshank on a post in the Avon valley. In all settings, the redshank is one of the most vocal, vigilant and nervous of birds with its distinctive high fluting calls. This species breeds in a variety of wetland habitats including coastal and flood plain grazing marshes. Due to wetland drainage for agriculture, the species declined after the 1960s.

The Avon Valley in Hampshire and Dorset supports important areas of a range of semi-natural flood plain habitats including flower-rich meadows and pastures, marshy grasslands and mires. The sand and gravel river terraces also support areas of acid grassland.

several Redshanks
on posts - nests
nearby?

Avon valley June·08
John Davis

two whoopers feeding with sheep, Perthshire May

Water meadows

Although not strictly falling within the definition of semi-natural old meadows, water meadows date from the 16th century and are a type of grassland management that uses controlled flooding or irrigation (often termed drowning or floating) and draining to promote early grass growth and/or increased annual grass production. This is usually effected through a complex of channels (termed carriers, gutters) and sluices and hatches.

Given that they are regularly inundated with warming, relatively nutrient-rich water, the sward of the few remaining working water meadows is often fertile and lush and is primarily composed of various grasses including the hybrid fescue which is a cross between meadow fescue (Festuca pratensis) and perennial rye-grass (Lolium perenne). Herbaceous plants tend to be common species such as creeping buttercup (*Ranunculus repens*), white clover and dandelions (*Taraxacum* sp).

Occasionally small areas of less-fertile, damper grassland may occur adjacent to ditches and carriers and contain species such as water avens (*Geum rivale*), ragged robin and marsh marigold.

Although the wildlife value of working water meadows may not be high, such meadows do have considerable heritage value as examples of agricultural archaeology.

Whooper swans, Perthshire
Two whooper swans (Eala-fhiadhaich) grazing with sheep in a Perthshire pasture in May. This species of conservation concern is a winter visitor to Great Britain. It is known that most of the birds that winter in Britain breed in Iceland during the summer. A summer plumage male golden plover completes the scene.

Previous page
Cattle and yellow wagtails
Yellow wagtails and grazing cattle. This species is a summer visitor to Great Britain. The highest breeding densities occur in cattle-grazed wet lowland grasslands. Yellow wagtails can often be seen in association with cattle. As they graze, the cattle disturb insects such as dung flies, which provides valued insect food for the birds.

Meadow brown butterflies
The meadow brown butterfly is a common and widespread species of grasslands and other open vegetation but it is not restricted to semi-natural habitats. It occurs throughout Great Britain except on the tops of higher mountains. The caterpillars feed on a wide variety of grasses.

Roadside verges

Road verges normally comprise grassland vegetation that is periodically mown. They have been estimated to cover an area of more than 200,000 hectares across Great Britain. The grassland of the majority of road verges is dominated by the tall, coarse false oat-grass (*Arrhenatherum elatius*) which thrives under a regular cutting regime in the absence of any grazing by livestock. This vegetation can be very variable in its composition, ranging from species-poor with just a few coarse grasses and tall herbs such as hogweed (*Heracleum sphondylium*) to grassland that is moderately rich in species (10-20 in a square metre), with a selection of species typical of old meadows and pastures and calcareous grassland such as common knapweed, greater knapweed (*Centaurea scabiosa*), lady's bedstraw, yellow meadow vetchling, bird's-foot trefoil and meadowsweet. One species that seems to have a particular preference for roadside verges is meadow cranesbill (*Geranium pratense*).

Roadside verges that support vegetation similar to that of, in particular, old meadows and pastures and calcareous grassland are of particular significance in intensive agricultural areas, where semi-natural examples of these habitats are very rare. For example, in some parts of northern England, roadside verges are an important reservoir of typical upland hay meadow (old meadows and pastures) species such as wood cranesbill, melancholy thistle, water avens and great burnet. In some parts of eastern and central England on chalk or limestone rocks, roadside verges support important remnants of calcareous grassland which have become rare in the farmed countryside. This is particularly the case in counties such as Lincolnshire, Leicestershire and Rutland.

Grey partridges

A covey of grey partridges in winter. The favoured habitat of this species is mixed lowland farmland with arable, permanent grassland and hedgerows. They also inhabit landscapes with semi-natural habitats such as calcareous grassland and lowland heathland. Salisbury Plain, which is a very large expanse of calcareous grassland, holds between two and three hundred pairs. Numbers have declined massively since World War II. The reasons for the decline are complex but relate to factors associated with the increasing intensification of agriculture, for example, loss and degradation of farmland habitats and the increased use of pesticides.

Map showing a selection of Nature Reserves in Great Britain with wildflower grasslands as listed in the Gazeteer

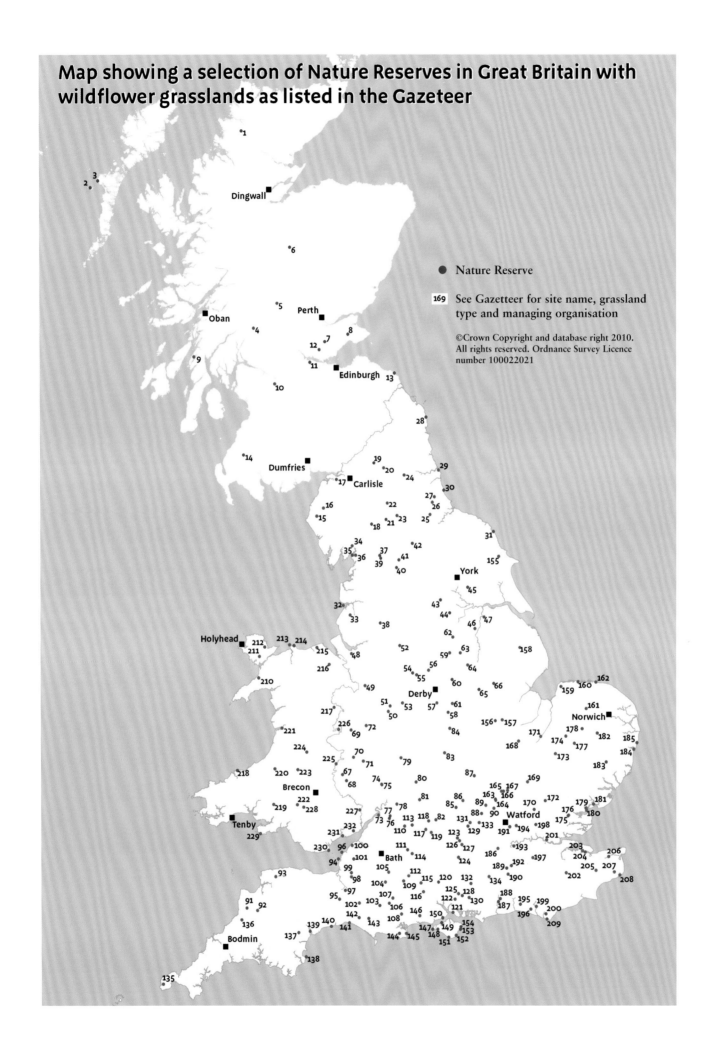

● Nature Reserve

169 See Gazetteer for site name, grassland type and managing organisation

A selection of Nature Reserves in Great Britain containing areas of semi-natural (wildflower) grassland*

Grass-land type (see key below)	English Region/Country										
	NE	NW	Y/H	WM	EM	EAST	SE	SW	LONDON	WALES	SCOTLAND
OMP	22 Moor House-Upper Teesdale[1] (D) 23 Hannah's Meadow[6] (D) 24 South Close Field[6] (N)	Gowk Bank[1] (C) 15 High Leys[1] (C) 16 Sandy Beck Meadow[1] (C) 21 Augill Pasture[6,14] (C)	Lower Derwent Valley /Wheldrake Ings[1,6] (NY/EY) 40 New House Meadows[1,4] (NY) 41 Malham & Upper Wharfedale[1,4] (NY) 42 Leyburn Glebe[6] (NY)	83 Draycote Meadows[6] (Wk) 79 Fosters Green Meadows[1] (Wo) 50 Mottey Meadows[1] (St) 49 Melverley Farm[6] (Sh) 67 The Sturts North[6] (Hr)	60 Bulwell Hall Park Meadows[20] (NtC) 65 Muston Meadows[1] (Le) 61 Loughborough Big Meadow[6] (Le) 64 Eakring Meadow[6] (Nt) 87 Mill Crook and Grafton Regis Meadow[6] (No) 56 Rose End Meadows[6] (D) 46 Rush Furlong[6] (Li)	183 Fox Fritillary Meadow[6] (Sk) 172 Hatfield Forest[4] (E) 176 118 Hitchcocks Meadows[6] (E) 161 Hoe Rough[6] (Nr) 170 Hunsdon Mead[6] (He) 163 Lancot Meadow[6] (B) 89 Millhoppers Pasture[17] (He) 182 New Buckenham Common[6] (Nr) 198 Roding Valley Meadows[20] (E) 168 Upwood Meadows[1,6] (C)	71 Ashford Hill[1] (H) 82 Chimney Meadows[1,6] (O) 118 Grafton Lock Meadow[4] (O) 149 Isle of Wight – Newtown[4] (IOW) 202 Marden Meadow[6] (K) 186 Thorpe Hay Meadow[6] (Su) 86 Long Herdon and Grange Meadows[6,14] (Bu) 127 Moor Copse[6] (Be) Ron Ward's Meadow[6] (H)	95 Barrington Hill[1] (Sm) 110 Clattinger Farm[1,6] (W) 102 Hardington Moor[1] (Sm) 137 Ruggadon Middlepark[6] (Dv) 81 Greystones Farm[6] (G) 113 North Meadow, Cricklade[1] (W) 99 Somerset Levels[1] (Sm) 142 South Poorton Reserve[6,19] (Dt)	191 Bentley Priory[20] 194 Totteridge Fields[6]	228 Berthlwyd Farm, Brecon[4] (P) 210 Caeau Tan y Bwlch[14] (Gw) 220 Caeau Llety Cybi[8] (Ce) 219 Carmel[3,19] (Cm) 212 Cors Goch[3,13] (Gw) 224 Gilfach Farm[9] (P) 217 Ty Brith[11] (P) 227 Pentwyn Farm[12] (M)	11 Bo'mains Meadow[7] (F) 14 Feoch meadows[7] (SA) 12 Lielowan Meadow[7] (Fi) 10 West Kittochside[16] (Gc)
CG	27 Cassop Vale[1] (D) 30 Durham Coast[4] (D) 20 Hadrians's Wall Estate[4] (N) 28 Northumberland Coast[4] (N) 26 Thrislington[1] (D) 29 The Leas & Marsden Rock[4] (Tyne & Wear)	35 Arnside-Silverdale[4] (C) 36 Gait Barrows[1] (C) 18 Great Asby Scar[1] (C) 38 Nob End[20] (GM) 34 Whitbarrow[6] (C)	155 Fordon Chalk Bank[6] (NY) 39 Ingleborough[1] (NY) 37 Southerscales[1,6] (NY) 41 Malham & Upper Wharfedale[4] (NY) 44 Thompson Meadow[6,14] (NY) 43 Townclose Hills[20] (Ld) 31 Yorkshire Coast[4] (NY)	54 Hamps & Manifold[4] (St) 72 Wenlock Edge[4] (Sh)	66 Ancaster Valley[6] (Li) Bulwell Hall Park Meadows[20] (NtC) 156 Collyweston Quarries[6] (No) 55 Derbyshire Dales & Dovedale & Biggindale[1,4] (D) 59 Hollinhill & Markland Grips[6] (D) 158 Red Hill[6] (Li)	157 Barnack Hills & Holes[1] (P) 166 Barton Hills[1] (B) 164 Dunstable Downs[4] (B) 167 Knocking Hoe[1] (B) 159 Ringstead Downs[6] (Nr) 165 Sharpenhoe Clappers[4] (B) 177 Thetford Heath[1] (Sk) 174 Weeting Heath[1] (Nr) 169 Therfield Heath[4] (He)	90 Ashridge Estate[4] (H) Afton, Compton & Brook Downs[4] (IoW) 131 Aston Rowant[1] (O) 126 Basildon Park[4] (Be) 125 Beacon Hill (H) 209 Birling Gap[4] (ES) 192 Box Hill[4] (S) 130 Butser Hill (H)[1,20] 196 Castle Hill[1] (ES) 88 Coombe Hill & Low Scrubs[4] (Bu) 133 Bradenham Estate[4] (Bu) 129 Watlington Hill[4] (O) 195 Devil's Dyke, Fulking Escarpment & Newtimber Hill[4] (WS) 189 Hackhurst /White Downs[4] (Su) 147 Isle of Wight: The Needles to Tennyson Down[4] (IoW) 152 Isle of Wight: Ventnor Down[4] (IoW)	145 Ballard Down[4] (Dt) 138 Berry Head-Sharkham Point[1] (Dv) 140 Branscombe & Salcombe Regis[4] (Dv) 94 Brean Down[4] (Sm) 111 Cherhill Down & Oldbury Castle[4] (W) 105 Cley Hill[4] (W) 78 Crickley Hill[4] (G) 101 Dolebury Warren[4] (Sm) 80 Dover's Hill[4] (G) 115 Figsbury Ring[4] (W) 107 Fontmell & Melbury Down, Dorset Hill-forts[4] (Dt) 106 Hod Hill & Hambledon Hill[1,4] (Dt) 143 Hog Cliff[1] (Dt) 108 Kingston Lacy Estate[4] (Dt) 96 Middle Hope & Sand Point[4] (Sm) (Avon) 112 Parsonage Down[1] (W) 116 Pepperbox Hill[4] (W)	197 Saltbox Hill[6]	219 Carmel[3,19] (Cm) 215 Graig Fawr: Dyserth[4] (De) 229 Gower Cliffs/Gower Coast[3,4] (Sw) 230 Lavernock Point[4,8] (Vg) 216 Loggerheads Country Park[20] (De) 214 Rhiwledyn (Little Orme)[4,13] (Cw) 213 Gogarth (Great Orme)[4,13] (Cw) 232 Rogiet Poor Land Reserve[12] (M) 222 Craig y Rhiwarth[10] (P)	5 Ben Lawers[2,16] (Hi) 8 Fleecefaulds Meadow[7] (Fi) 4 Glencoe (Meall Mor) (Hi)[9] 1 Inchna damph[2] (Hi) 13 St Abbs Head (S)[2,16]

Continued on next page

Grass-land type (see key below)	NE	NW	Y/H	WM	EM	EAST	SE	SW	LONDON	WALES	SCOTLAND
CG Cont.							148 Isle of Wight: Compton Down[4] (IoW) 153 Isle of Wight: Bembridge & Culver Downs[4] (IoW) 151 Isle of Wight: St Catherine's Point to St Helens[4] (IoW) 208 Langdon Cliffs[4] (K) 123 Lardon Chase & Lough Down[4] (Be) 199 Lewes Downs[1] (ES) 200 Lullington Heath[1] (ES) 207 Lydden & Temple Ewell Downs[1] (K) 128 Old Winchester Hill[4] (H) 120 Stockbridge Down[4] (H) 119 White Horse Hill[4] (O) 134 Witley & Milford Commons[4] (Su) 205 Wye[1] (K)	114 Pewsey Downs[1] (W) 77 Rodborough Common[4] (G) 76 Minchinhampton Common[4] (G) The Hollies, Lardon Chase & Lough Down[4] (Be) 104 White Sheet Down[4] (W) 109 Wylye Down[1] (W)			
AG	Hadrains's Wall Estate[4] (N)	52 Lyme Park[4] (Ch)	62 Maltby Low Common[6] (SY)	70 Croft Castle[4] (He) 74 Malvern Hills: Midsummer Hill (Wo/Hr) 75 Malvern Hills: Tack Coppice[4] (Wo/Hr) 69 Long Mynd[4] (Sh) 53 Shugborough Estate & Great Haywood Bank[4] (St)	47 Atkinson's Warren[20] (LiN) 63 Clumber Park[4] (N) 57 Calke Abbey[4] (D) 58 Ulverscroft[4] (L) 84 Croft Pasture[6] (Le)	Thetford Heath[1] (Sk) 184 Minsmere/ Westleton Heaths[1,5] (Sk) 175 Danbury & Lingwood Commons[4] (E)	191 Leith Hill[4] (Su) 146 New Forest Commons[4] (H) 132 Sclbournc Common[4] (H)	135 Chapel Caren Brea[4] (Co) 144 Corfe Castle[4] (Dt) 141 Golden Cap[4] (Dt)	193 Richmond Park[1]	219 Carmel[3,19] (Cm) 224 Gilfach Farm[9] (P) 218 Mynachdy'r Graig[15] (Ce) 226 Roundton Hill[11] (P) 225 Stanner Rocks[3] (P) 223 Vicarage meadows[10] (P)	
MG	25 Redcar Field[6] (D)	17 Finlandrigg Woods[1] (C) 19 Gowk Bank[1] (C)	45 Lower Derwent Valley[1] (NY/EY) 51 Allimore Green[6] (St)	68 The Flits[1] (Hr)		174 Chippenham Fen[1] (Ca) 178 Thompson Common[6] (Nr)	85 Otmoor[5] (O) 117 Tuckmill Meadow[6] (O) 178 New Forest Commons[4] (H) 124 Ron Ward's Meadow[6] (H) 122 The Moors, Bishop Waltham (H)[20]	93 Arlington[4] (Dv) 91 Dunsdon Farm[1,6] (Dv) 92 Dunsland Park[4] (Dv) 100 Gordano Valley[1] (Sm) 136 Greena Moor[6,14] (Co) 103 Haddon Moor[17] (Sm) 98 Shapwick Heath[1] (Sm) 97 Somerset levels/West Sedgemoor[1,5] (Sm)			9 Taynish[2] (A) Loch Lomond[2] (A)

156

						English Region/Country					
Grass-land type (see key below)	NE	NW	Y/H	WM	EM	EAST	SE	SW	LONDON	WALES	SCOTLAND
CFGM		48 Gowy Meadows[6] (Ch) 32 Ribble Estuary[1] (L) 33 Martin Mere (L)[18]	Lower Derwent Valley /Wheldrake Ings[1,6] (NY/EY)			185 Benacre[1] (Sk) 181 Colne Estuary[1] (E) 160 Holkham[1] (Nr) 171 Ouse Washes/Welney[5,18] 179 Old Hall Marshes[5] (E) 180 Tollesbury Wick[6] (E) 201 Rainham Marshes[5] (E) 162 Salthouse Marshes[6] (Nr)	203 Elmley Marshes[1,5] (K) 150 North Solent[1] (H) 188 Pulborough Brooks[5] (WS) 187 Amberley Wild Brooks[5] (WS) 206 Stodmarsh[1] (K) 204 The Swale[1] (K) 121 Titchfield Haven[1,20] (H) 154 Brading Marshes[5] (IOW)	139 Exe Estuary[3] (Dv) 73 Slimbridge[18] (G) 99 Somerset levels - Tadham[1] (Sm)		211 Malltraeth Marsh[5] (Gw) 231 Newport Wetlands[3] (M) 221 Ynys-hir[5] (Ce)	6 Insh marshes (Hi)[2,5]
Machair											3 Balranald (Wi)[5] 2 Monach Isles (Wi)[2]

OMP = Old meadows & pastures
CG = Calcareous grassland (including chalk & limestone grassland)
AG = Acid grassland
MG = Marshy grassland (Purple moor-grass and rush pastures)
CFGM = Coastal & flood-plain grazing marsh

*Always check access arrangements – some reserves may have restrictions on the time of visit, special arrangements for visiting during the bird breeding season or may require permits from the appropriate authority.

Local Authority (England)

B	Bedfordshire	Ld	Leeds
Be	Berkshire	Le	Leicestershire
Bu	Buckinghamshire	Li	Lincolnshire
Ca	Cambridgeshire	LiN	North Lincolnshire
C	Cumbria	N	Northumberland
Ch	Cheshire	No	Northamptonshire
Co	Cornwall	Nr	Norfolk
D	Derbyshire	Nt	Nottinghamshire
Dt	Dorset	NtC	Nottingham City
Dv	Devon	NY	North Yorkshire
E	Essex	O	Oxfordshire
ES	East Sussex	Sh	Shropshire
EY	East Yorkshire	Sm	Somerset
G	Gloucestershire	St	Staffordshire
GM	Greater Manchester	Su	Surrey
H	Hampshire	SY	South Yorkshire
He	Hertfordshire	Wk	Warwickshire
Hr	Herefordshire	W	Wiltshire
IoW	Isle of Wight	WS	West Sussex
K	Kent	Wo	Worcestershire
L	Lancashire		

Wales

Ce	Ceredigion
Cm	Carmarthenshire
Cw	Conwy
De	Denbighshire
Gw	Gwynedd
M	Monmouthshire
P	Powys
Pm	Pembrokeshire
Sw	Swansea
Vg	Vale of Glamorgan

Scotland

A	Argyll and Bute
F	Falkirk
Fi	Fife
Gc	Glasgow City
Hi	Highland
S	Scottish Borders
SA	South Ayrshire
Wi	Western Isles

1	Natural England
2	Scottish Natural Heritage
3	Countryside Council for Wales
4	National Trust
5	RSPB
6	Wildlife Trust (England)
7	Scottish Wildlife Trust
8	South & West Wales Wildlife Trust
9	Radnorshire Wildlife Trust
10	Brecknock Wildlife Trust
11	Montgomery Wildlife Trust
12	Gwent Wildlife Trust
13	North Wales Wildlife Trust
14	Plantlife
15	National Trust
16	National Trust for Scotland
17	Butterfly Conservation
18	Wildfowl and Wetlands Trust
19	The Grasslands Trust
20	Local Authority Local Nature Reserve (LNR)

Further information – see the following websites

Natural England http://www.naturalengland.org.uk/ourwork/conservation/designatedareas/nnr/default.aspx
Scottish Natural Heritage http://www.nnr-scotland.org.uk/findnnr.asp
Countryside Council for Wales http://www.ccw.gov.uk/landscape—wildlife/protecting-our-landscape/special-landscapes—sites/protected-landscapes/national-nature-reserves.aspx
Royal Society for the Protection of Birds http://www.rspb.org.uk/reserves/
The Wildlife Trusts (England) http://www.wildlifetrusts.org/ The website has a link to find an individual English local Wildlife Trust as follows:
http://www.wildlifetrusts.org/index.php?section=localtrusts
Scottish Wildlife Trust http://www.swt.org.uk/
South & West Wales Wildlife Trust http://www.welshwildlife.org/
Radnorshire Wildlife Trust http://www.radnorshirewildlifetrust.org.uk/
Brecknock Wildlife Trust http://www.brecknockwildlifetrust.org.uk/
Montgomery Wildlife Trust http://www.montwt.co.uk/
Gwent Wildlife Trust http://www.gwentwildlife.org/
North Wales Wildlife Trust http://www.northwaleswildlifetrust.org.uk/english/page_home.php
Plantlife http://www.plantlife.org.uk/nature_reserves
National Trust http://www.nationaltrust.org.uk/main/
National Trust for Scotland http://www.nts.org.uk/Home/
Butterfly Conservation http://www.butterfly-conservation.org/text/6/conservation.html
Wildfowl and Wetlands Trust http://www.wwt.org.uk/
The Grasslands Trust http://www.grasslands-trust.org/

Plantlife-owned reserves are usually managed by the relevant Local Wildlife Trust. Some National Nature Reserves declared by the statutory conservation agencies in Great Britain are owned and managed by other organisations such as a Wildlife Trust, the National Trust or Local Authorities. Some Local Authority owned reserves are managed by Wildlife Trusts or National Trust. In all of these situations both organisations are credited in the footnote/key

There are a large number of Local Nature Reserves some of which have semi-natural grassland and are accessible to urban centres – see following web link for details:-

http://www.lnr.naturalengland.org.uk/Special/lnr/lnr_search.asp

Grassland names and terms

Aftermath, also Foggage, Fog, Eddish
The re-growth of grass in a meadow that has been cut for hay or silage and then used either for grazing livestock or for another crop of grass in silage systems. Traditionally, stock were allowed in after six weeks (see also **lammas meadow**).

Balk/Baulk
A ridge, piece or strip of land left unploughed (usually grassland).

Bawk meadow
A series of ditched enclosures where cattle are pastured in summer.

Brooks
A Sussex term which refers to flat, open extensive land on river floodplains in the valleys of the River Arun, at Amberley, and the River Ouse, near Lewes. They comprise rough pasture or meadows edged by drainage ditches and are often subject to seasonal flooding (see also the description of coastal and flood plain grazing marsh).
Examples: Amberley Wild Brooks, Pulborough Brooks.

Cae, Caeau (pl) (Welsh)
Field, enclosure.

Close
An enclosure.
Example: Moor Closes (Lincolnshire).

Cluain (Gaelic)
A meadow.

*Clun (Welsh)
Meadow, moor.

Culm grassland
In north Devon and Cornwall, the term "Culm grassland" has been coined for marshy grasslands and wet heaths occurring over the rocks of the Culm measures.

Cytir (Welsh)
Common pasture.

Dôl, Dolau, Dolydd (pl) (Welsh)
Meadow.

Down, Downland
An undulating tract of grassland (pasture) land, especially on the chalk of southern England, traditionally used for grazing sheep and cattle. Examples: Wye & Crundale Downs (Kent), Lewes Downs (East Sussex).

Dry Matter content (DM)
The dry matter component of the commodity or feed (e.g. hay or silage) which includes all the solid components except the moisture/water content. It is usually expressed as a percentage.

Ensile
To turn harvested green fodder (especially grass) into **silage** by causing it to ferment in an airtight environment (e.g. a silo or plastic bag).

Flood meadow
A low-lying area of meadow adjacent to a watercourse that periodically floods during periods of heavy rainfall especially in the autumn and winter. Example: Castor flood meadows (Peterborough).

There is a distinction between the terms '**flood meadow**' and '**water meadow**'; the latter is a human-made system of irrigation controlled by the farmer (see below).

Forb
Any herbaceous plant other than a grass.

Ffridd
Upland fringe in Wales between the inbye land and open mountain, comprising a mixture of grassland, heathland, scattered trees and bracken, usually used for rough grazing.

Forage
A crop (such as grass) consumed in the green state by livestock or made into hay or silage.

Gair
A grassy spot.

Garth
A small piece of enclosed land (usually grassland) next to a farmhouse or other dwelling. Mostly a term used in northern England. Also used in Wales (Garth – enclosure or promontory).

Glebe
An area of cultivated land, a field. It can include land managed as grassland.
Examples: Leyburn Glebe (North Yorkshire).

Glaswellt / Glaswelltir (Welsh)
Grass, grassland.

Gwair (Welsh)
Hay.

Gwaun, Gweunydd (pl) (Welsh)
Moor, meadow or mountain pasture.

Gweirglodd, gweirgoddiau (pl) (Welsh)
Hay meadow.

Gwyndwn, Gwndwn (Welsh)
Grassland, permanent pasture.

Haining
Enclosed land, meadow.

Ham/Hamm
This is often interpreted as water meadow or a pasture or meadow enclosed by a ditch or an enclosure in the bend of a river. However, some authorities state that it merely means a place on a flood plain. It is difficult to separate from the more common 'Ham', which means home or settlement. Hamm tends to be commonest in south-west England. Example: Upton Ham (Worcestershire).

Haugh, Heugh (Scottish or northern English)
A low-lying meadow adjacent to a watercourse or between hills. It came to mean any land by a stream or river.

Hay
Dried grass /herbage cut from a **meadow** in summer and stored for later use as winter feed for livestock.

Haylage
A grass crop that is generally cut earlier than **hay** and is baled and then preserved in an airtight environment (e.g. plastic wrapped) at a higher moisture content than hay but lower than **silage**.

Hayward
An officer of a manor, township, parish or the governing committee/court of a lammas/common meadow whose role is to supervise meadow management, in particular grazing and haymaking. In particular, this may involve ensuring that fences, hedges or other barriers are secure to prevent livestock from entering land shut up to grow hay.

Haysel
The hay making season.

Heath
Older definitions were broader in scope including all open, more or less flat uncultivated rough grazing land or "wasteland" including grassland (e.g. the Lincoln Heath). Currently, it is more usually applied to land covered with vegetation with a high cover of ericaceous species such as ling (*Calluna vulgaris*), bell heather (*Erica cinerea*) or bilberry (*Vaccinium myrtillus*). Examples: Breckland Heaths, Weeting Heath (Norfolk), Thetford Heaths (Suffolk).

Herb
A non-woody seed-bearing plant.

Herbaceous
Composed of soft, green non-woody tissue.

Holm(e)
Two specific definitions are a 'meadow on the shore' and 'water meadow'. Other definitions include "a small island or a drier place especially in a river, estuary or lake" and "stretch of low-lying land beside a river". Example: Portholme (Cambridgeshire). **Ynys** is probably the Welsh equivalent.

Inch, Innis, Inish
An island, pasture land near water.

Ings
Grassland, meadow or pasture or, more rarely, fen or swamp, usually managed for hay cropping, situated next to a river or stream and often subject to flooding. A common name used in central and northern England. Examples: Derwent Ings (North and East Yorkshire), Aubert Ings (North Yorkshire).

Lag/Lagg
A Sussex term for a long, marshy meadow.

Lammas or Common meadows[1]
Meadows where the land is divided into strips or doles, each mown for hay by a different farmer. In some meadows an individual always owned the same strip, but on some, lots were cast each year before hay cutting to determine who should have which strip for that year. After the hay cut, the meadow is then available for communal or common grazing on Lammas Day (now 1st August but August 12th until 1752). The name Lammas derives from the loaf mass held to mark the start of the corn harvest rather than the end of hay making. Grazing normally continues until Candlemas day (February 2nd), although the practice varies from place to place. Interestingly most lammas meadows are situated on flat land adjacent to rivers and streams. In the past, land adjacent to watercourses was the obvious place to locate meadows, as the land is naturally fertile due to regular deposition of nutrient-rich silt following flooding. In addition, this land was less suitable for arable cultivation due to flooding.

Examples of Lammas meadows: North Meadow, Cricklade, Pixey and Yarnton Meads, Oxfordshire.

Laich meadow
A dry, dunged meadow.

Lawn
The original definition of a lawn was grassland or an open area within a Forest[2] open to grazing throughout the year. An equivalent term is Plain.
Areas of grassland within the New Forest (Hampshire) are still referred to as lawns.

Now, the term lawn is normally used to denote an area of land established by the sowing of grass (and sometimes other plants such as clover) or the laying of turves that is subsequently maintained at a low, even height by regular mowing. Most commonly, lawns are associated with domestic dwellings where they are used for informal recreation or are merely for decorative purposes.

Lea
Grassland (meadow or pasture). Examples: Catton Lea Meadow (Northumberland).

Leaze
Pasture, meadow of which **Leasow** is an inflexion[3]. It is not the plural of lea or ley. Example: Upham Meadow and Summer Leasow (Gloucestershire/Herefordshire and Worcestershire).

Levancy and Couchancy
The principle of levancy and couchancy determines the number of livestock that can be sustained on common pasture during the winter months.

Levels
A term sometimes specifically applied to flat, open extensive land on river floodplains comprising pasture or meadows edged by drainage ditches and often subject to seasonal flooding. Example: Somerset Levels.

Ley
Land that is temporarily grassland, and therefore similar to **improved grassland** (q.v.), but which alternates with periods of arable cultivation.

Mead
A meadow. The Old English *maēd* is derived from the verb *māwan* to mow. Examples: Pixey and Yarnton Meads, Wendlebury Meads (both Oxfordshire).

Meadow
An area of grassland. In its original sense, the term meadow was used to denote grassland where the grass is allowed to grow up and then cut for hay in summer. Grazing animals are temporarily excluded during this "shut up" period. Grazing may take place before "shut up/put up" for hay in spring and/or after the hay has been cut in summer (aftermath grazing). However, more recently the term meadow has been used more loosely to denote any area of grassland regardless of management. Examples: North Meadow, Cricklade (Wiltshire), Barrington Hill Meadows (Somerset).

Pasture
Land used for all or part of the year for forage for livestock (but not cut for hay – see **meadow**). It is not necessarily confined to grassland and could, for example, include land where grassland forms a mosaic with other types of vegetation such as bracken or ericaceous heath.

Permanent pasture
Land used to grow grasses or other herbaceous forage either naturally (self-seeded) or through cultivation (sown), which has not been ploughed and reseeded for five years or more.

Pightle, Pyghtle (and other variants)
A small field or enclosure; a small meadow, a close or croft.

Pingle
A small enclosed piece of land; a paddock, a close.

Pleck
In the Wyre Forest, the local name for very small meadows near the Dowles Brook is 'Pleck'. It probably means a small parcel of land, often grassland but possibly periodically cultivated.

Porfa, Tir Pori (Welsh)
Pasture.

Rhôs, Rhostir (Welsh)
Moor, heath or marshland. In Wales, marshy grassland pastures (see description of marshy grassland) are often referred to as **Rhôs pastures**. This latter term was first coined in the mid 1970s by Chris Fuller of the then Nature Conservancy Council (see Pryce 2006).

Ridge and furrow (grassland)
Pasture fields that consist of wave-like undulations of ridges and furrows. These result from a particular method of ancient ploughing by oxen. From above, the ridge and furrow shows a characteristic reverse-S pattern caused by the wide turn of the plough needed at the end of each furrow. Ridge and furrow has survived where the patterns have been preserved by the later establishment of pasture or parkland, often following depopulation following the Black Death in the 14th century. Ridge and furrow fields are especially widespread in central and northern England.

Rispie
Long coarse grass.

Sheiling, Shealing
Usually defined as a temporary summer dwelling/hut in an upland or mountain area used when grazing domesticated animals on summer pastures. Sometimes the term is also used to cover both the dwelling and the associated high pasture. A similar Gaelic term is **Alrldh** or **Airle**.

Silage
Grass or other forage crop harvested in a green state that is subsequently preserved by fermentation in an airtight environment (in a silo, in a clamp or in large polythene bags). It is used as winter feed for livestock. A relatively modern innovation, first introduced into Britain in the late 1800s but not widely adopted until the 1970s. It is now the main system (replacing hay) for producing conserved grass for winter livestock feed, especially on agriculturally improved grasslands.

Silwair (Welsh)
Silage.

Slade, Slate
Low-lying wet meadow or marsh land, a strip of greensward or of boggy land. Other definitions include a forest glade and a piece of level ground.

Soum
A unit of pasture that supported a finite number of livestock at different times over the course of a year, usually equivalent to the grass requirements of one cow.

Swale
To burn grassland or heathland.

Sward
The mixture of grasses and other plants covering the ground in a meadow or pasture.

Swath
A band or row of grass/herbage cut by a mower (or in the past a scythe) lying on the ground in a meadow.

Ted, Tedding
To toss **swaths** of newly-mown grass/herbage during hay making in order to expose more of the grass/herbage to the sun and air to quicken the drying process.

*Ton, Tonnau (pl) (Welsh)
Grassland or lea.

*Tonnen, Tonnenydd (pl) (Welsh)
Sward or bog.

*Tyno (Welsh)
Meadow, field, hollow.

Tywarchen (Welsh)
Sward, turf.

*Twyndir (Welsh)
Downland.

Warping
The process of deliberately flooding agricultural land, including grassland, in order to deposit silt (warp) carried by tidal rivers to enrich the soil. This practice was once common in the Isle of Axholme.

Washland/Washes
Low-lying land adjacent to a watercourse comprising grassland, fen or swamp which has been engineered to provide storage of flood water at times of high river flows (usually in autumn and winter), thus preventing flooding of cropland. Examples: Ouse Washes, Nene Washes (Cambridgeshire).

Waste
Unimproved common pasture; a source of turf for fuel.

Water meadow
A system of grassland management dating from the 16th century that uses controlled flooding or irrigation (often termed **drowning** or **floating**) and draining to promote early grass growth and/or increased annual grass production. This is usually effected through a complex of channels (termed carriers, gutters) and sluices and hatches. There are two main types: Bedwork systems are located on flat land adjacent to rivers, whereas Catchwork systems are found on hillsides and use gravity to move water downhill. Examples (Bedwork types): Britford water meadows, Lower Woodford water meadows (both Wiltshire).

Windflower meadow
A meadow that has abundant wood anemone (windflower) (*Anemone nemorosa*). This term has been used in upland regions of northern England, especially Cumbria. Such upland hay meadows with windflower are now very rare. A surviving example is Sandybeck Meadow (Cumbria).

Windrow
A row of hay (or other cut crop) consisting of two or more **swaths**.

Ynys, Ynys oedd (pl) (Welsh)
Island, holm, promontory, (river meadow?).

Ynys, Ynys oedd (pl) (Welsh)
Island, holm.

Ystrad (Welsh)
Valley, holm, river meadow.

---

[1] A common meadow is a specific example of one type of common land. In general terms, common land is land owned by one person over which another person is entitled to exercise rights of common (such as grazing animals or cutting bracken for livestock bedding), and these rights are generally exercisable in common with others. In addition, Halsbury's *The Laws of England* defines the right of common in Cooke's Inclosure Acts (4th Edition) as: "*A right, which one or more persons may have, to take or use some portion of that which another man's soil naturally produces*". Common land may then be defined as any land which is subject to such a right.

[2] Forest is used here in the medieval sense as land on which the king had the right to keep deer – it may be completely open or partly wooded.

[3] A change in the form of a word (usually by adding a suffix) to indicate a change in its grammatical function.

* Historical usage.

Welsh Rhôs Pasture, Bryncarnau, Rhondda , Cynon, Taff
A flower-rich Welsh Rhôs pasture. The purple flowers of meadow thistle (Ysgallen Mignwern), a very characteristic plant of these rushy marshy grasslands, are dotted throughout the sward. It is accompanied by bog asphodel (Llafn y Bladur) with its bronze-yellow flowers in the foreground, heath spotted orchids (Tegeirian Brych), meadow buttercup (Blodyn Ymenyn) and the delicate quaking grass (Crydwellt Mwyal). The last-named is sometimes referred to as doddering dillies. Two red kites (Barcud Coch) can be seen overhead.

References and selected reading

Angus, S. 2001. *The Outer Hebrides: Moor and Machair.* White Horse Press, Isle of Harris and Cambridge.

Asher, J., Warren, M.S., Fox, R., Harding, P., Jeffcoate, G. & Jeffcoate, S. 2001 *The Millennium Atlas of Butterflies in Britain and Ireland.* Oxford University Press, Oxford.

Babington, C.C. 1860. *Flora of Cambridgeshire.* J. van Voorst, London.

Beebee, T.J. & Griffiths, R.A. 2000 *Amphibians and reptiles: A natural history of the British Herpetofauna.* Harper Collins, London.

Benton, T. 2006 *Bumblebees: The natural history and identification of the species found in Britain.* Harper Collins, London.

Brassley, P. 1996 Silage in Britain, 1880—1990: The delayed adoption of an innovation. *The Agricultural History Review* 44, 63-87.

Brown, A.F. & Grice, P.V. 2005 *Birds in England.* T & A D Poyser, London.

Cocker, M. & Mabey, R. 2005 *Birds Britannica.* Chatto & Windus, London.

Cook, H. & Williamson, T. eds 2007 *Water meadows history, ecology & conservation.* Wingather Press/Oxbow Books, Oxford.

Corbet, P. & Brooks, S. 2008 *Dragonflies.* Harper Collins, London.

Crofts, A. & Jefferson, R.G. 1999 The Lowland Grassland Management Handbook. English Nature/The Wildlife Trusts, Peterborough.

Everard, M. (ed) 2005 *Water meadows: Living treasures in the English Landscape.* Forrest Text, Tresaith, Cardigan.

Foley, M. & Clarke, S. 2005 *Orchids of the British Isles.* The Griffin Press, Maidenhead.

Forrester, R., Andrews, I., McInerny, C., Murray, R., McGowan, R., Zonfrillo, B., Betts, M., Jardine, D. & Grundy, D. 2007 eds *The Birds of Scotland.* Scottish Ornithologists' Club, Aberlady.

Fuller, R.J. 1982 *Bird habitats in Britain.* T & A. D. Poyser, Calton.

Fuller, R M 1987 The changing extent and conservation interest of lowland grasslands in England and Wales: a review of grassland surveys 1930-1984. *Biological Conservation* 40, 281-300.

Gamble, D. & St. Pierre, T. (eds) 2010 *Hay Time in the Yorkshire Dales.* Yorkshire Dales Millennium Trust/Scotforth Books, Clapham.

Gibbard, S. 2000 *The Ferguson Tractor Story.* Old Pond Publishing Ltd, Ipswich.

Gibson, D.J. 2008 *Grass and Grassland Ecology.* Oxford University Press, Oxford.

Gilbert, O. 2000 *Lichens.* Harper Collins, London.

Green, R. & Riley, H. 1999 *Corncrakes.* Scottish Natural Heritage Publications, Battleby.

Harris, S. & Yalden, D.W. (eds) 2008 *Mammals of the British Isles: Handbook,* 4th edition. The Mammal Society, Southampton.

Harvey, G. 2002 *The Forgiveness of Nature The Story of Grass.* Vintage. London.

Hewins, E. J., Pinches, C., Arnold, J., Lush, M., Robertson, H. J. & Escott, S. 2005. The condition of lowland BAP priority grasslands: results from a sample survey of non-statutory stands in England. *English Nature Research Report No. 636.* English Nature, Peterborough.

Hopkins, A. (ed) 2000 *Grass Its production and utilization.* 3rd edition. Blackwell Science, Oxford.

Hopkins, J.J. 1990 British Meadows and Pastures. *British Wildlife*, 1, 202-215.

Jefferson, R G 2007 Grassland ecosystem services: Can they help the case for conservation? *In*: J.J. Hopkins (ed) *High Value Grassland: providing biodiversity, a clean environment and premium products.* British Grassland Society Occasional Symposium No. 38. British Grassland Society, Cirencester. pp 23-27.

Love, J. 2003 *Machair.* Scotland's Living Landscapes Series. Scottish Natural Heritage, Perth. Downloadable from http://www.snh.org.uk/pdfs/publications/livinglandscapes/machair.pdf

Lovegrove, R., Williams, G. & Williams, I. 1994 *Birds in Wales.* T & A. D. Poyser, Calton.

Lusby, P. & Wright, J. 2001 *Scottish Wild Plants: Their history, ecology and conservation.* 2nd edition. Mercat Press, Edinburgh.

Mabey, R. 1997 *Flora Brittanica.* Sinclair-Stevenson, London.

Mabey, R. 1980 *The Common Ground: a place for nature in Britain's future?* Hutchinson, London.

Mabey, R. & Evans, A. 1989 *Flowering of Britain.* 2nd edition. Chatto & Windus, London.

Majerus, M.E.N. 2002 *Moths.* Harper Collins, London.

Marren, P. 1995 Harvests of Beauty: The conservation of Hay Meadows. *British Wildlife*, 6, 235-243.

Marren, P. 2002 *Nature conservation: A review of the conservation of wildlife in Britain 1950-2001.* Harper Collins, London.

Marren, P. 2005 *Britain's Rare Flowers.* Christopher Helm, London.

Marren, P. & Mabey, R. 2010 *Bugs Britannica.* Chatto & Windus, London.

Natural England 2008 *State of the Natural Environment 2008.* Natural England, Sheffield.

Peeters, A. 2004 *Wild and sown grasses. Profiles of a temperate species selection: ecology, biodiversity and use.* Food and Agricultural Organisation of the United Nations and Blackwell Publishing, Rome.

Peterken, G. 2009 Woodland origins of meadows. *British Wildlife*, 20, 161-170.

Plantlife 2002 *England's Green Unpleasant Land? – Why urgent action is needed to save England's wild flower grasslands.* Plantlife, London.

Porley, R. & Hodgetts, N. 2005 *Mosses and liverworts.* Harper Collins, London.

Pryce, R.D. 2005 The Rhos Pastures of South-west Wales and their Conservation. Presidential Address, 10th May 2003. *Watsonia* 25, 1-16.

Purseglove, J. 1988 *Taming of the Flood. History and Natural History of rivers and wetlands.* Oxford University Press, Oxford.

Rackham, O. 1997 *History of the Countryside.* 3rd edition. Phoenix Publishers, London.

Roberts, J. 2010 The flowering of Cross Fell: montane vegetation and foot-and-mouth. *British Wildlife*, 21, 161-167.

Spooner, B. & Roberts, P. 2005 *Fungi.* Harper Collins, London.

Thomas, J. & Lewington, R. 2010 *The Butterflies of Britain and Ireland*. British Wildlife Publishing, Milton on Stour, Dorset.

Verner, Y. 2005 *The English Meadow: A portrait of Country Life*. Green Books Ltd, Totnes.

Warren, P. 2010 Black Grouse recovery in northern England. *British Wildlife*, 21, 833-391.

Wilson, P. & King, M. 2003 *Arable plants – a field guide*. WILDGuides Ltd, Old Basing, Hampshire.

http://www.ukbap.org.uk/BAPGroupPage.aspx?id=98

There is no general authoritative publication aimed at the layperson describing the full range of Britain's wildflower grasslands. The only books that provide accounts of these grasslands are aimed at technical or academic audiences. For the reader who wishes to explore the more technical information then see:

Averis, A. M., Averis, A. B. G., Birks, H. J. B., Horsfield, D., Thompson, B. A. & Yeo, M. J. M. 2004 *An illustrated guide to British upland vegetation*. Joint Nature Conservation Committee, Peterborough.

Cooper, E. A. 1997 Summary descriptions of National Vegetation Classification grassland and montane communities. *UK Nature Conservation Report No. 14*. Joint Nature Conservation Committee, Peterborough.

Duffey, E., Morris M. G., Sheail, J., Ward, L. K., Wells, D. A. & Wells, T. C. E. 1974 *Grassland ecology and wildlife management*. Chapman and Hall, London.

Ratcliffe, D.A. 1977 *A Nature Conservation Review*. 2 Volumes. Cambridge University Press, Cambridge.

Rodwell, J. S. (ed) 1991. *British Plant Communities: Mires and Heaths*. Cambridge University Press, Cambridge. (Describes marshy grasslands).

Rodwell, J. S. (ed) 1992. *British Plant Communities: Grasslands and Montane Communities*. Cambridge University Press, Cambridge. (Describes calcareous, neutral (old meadows & pastures, grazing marshes) and acid grasslands).

Stevens, D.P., Smith, S.L.N., Blackstock, T.H., Bosanquet, S.D.S. & Stevens, J.P. 2010 *Grasslands of Wales: A survey of lowland species-rich grasslands, 1987-2004*. University of Wales Press, Cardiff.

Tansley, A.G. 1939 *The British Islands and their vegetation*. Cambridge University Press, Cambridge.
This book was reprinted in 2009 and can be purchased as 2 paperback volumes. Despite its age, the descriptions of the different British wildlife habitats including wildflower-rich grasslands remain useful.

Veen, P., Jefferson, R.G., de Smidt, J & van der Straaten, J. (eds) 2009 *Grasslands in Europe of High Nature Value*. KNNV Publishing, Zeist, The Netherlands.

Identification guides

Plants and fungi
Bon, M. 2007 *Mushrooms and toadstools of Britain and North-West Europe*. A & C Black Publishers Ltd, London.

Cope, T. & Gray, A.J. 2009 *Grasses of the British Isles*. Botanical Society of the British Isles, London.

Dobson, F. S. 2005 *Lichens: An Illustrated Guide to the British and Irish Species*. 5th edition. The Richmond Publishing Company, Slough.

Fitter, A., Fitter, R. & Farrer, A. 2002 *Collins Pocket Guide to Grasses Sedges Rushes and Ferns of Britain and Northern Europe*. Harper Collins, London.

Hubbard, C. 1992 *Grasses*. 3rd edition. Penguin Books, Harmondsworth.

Atherton, I., Bosanquet, S. & Lawley, M. 2010 *Mosses and Liverworts of Britain and Ireland. A Field Guide*. British Bryological Society.

Phillips, R. 2006 *Mushrooms*. Macmillan, London.

Poland, J. & Clement, E. 2009 *The Vegetative Key to the British Flora. A New Approach to Plant Identification*. Botanical Society of the British Isles, London.

Rose, F. 1989 *Colour identification guide to the grasses, sedges, rushes and ferns of the British Isles and North-western Europe*. Viking Books, London.

Rose, F. & O'Reilly, C. 2006 *The Wild Flower Key: How to identify wild flowers, trees and shrubs in Britain and Ireland*. Frederick Warne Books, London.

Stace, C. 2010 *New flora of the British Isles*. 3rd edition. Cambridge University Press, Cambridge.

Streeter, D. 2009 *Collins Flower Guide*. Collins, London.

Birds
Svensson, L., Mullarney, K., Zetterstrom, D. & Grant, P. J. 2010 *Collins Bird Guide. The Most Complete Guide to the Birds of Britain and Europe*. 2nd edition. Harper Collins, London.

Reptiles
Arnold, N. 2002 *Collins Field Guide to the Reptiles and Amphibians of Britain and Europe*. 2nd edition. Harper Collins, London.

Mammals
MacDonald, D. 2005 *Collins Field Guide to the Mammals of Britain and Europe*. Harper Collins, London.

Invertebrates
Brooks, S. 2002 *Field Guide to the Dragonflies and Damselflies of Great Britain and Ireland*. 2nd edition. British Wildlife Publishing, Gillingham, Dorset.

Cameron, R. & Riley, G. 2003 *Land Snails in the British Isles*. Field Studies Council Occasional Publication No. 79. Field Studies Council, Shrewsbury.

Chinery, M. 1997 *Collins Field Guide to the Insects of Britain and Northern Europe*. Harper Collins, London.

Edwards, M. & Jenner, M. 2009 *Field Guide to the Bumblebees of Great Britain and Ireland*. 2nd edition. Ocelli Limited, Eastbourne.

Evans, M. & Edmondson, R. J. 2007 *A Photographic Guide to the Grasshoppers and Crickets of Britain and Ireland*. WILDGuides Ltd, Old Basing, Hampshire.

Pinchen, B. J. 2006 *A Pocket Guide to the Grasshoppers, Crickets and Allied Insects of Britain and Ireland*. Forficula Books, Lymington.

Pinchen, B. J. 2006 *A Pocket Guide to the Bumblebees of Britain and Ireland*. Forficula Books, Lymington.

Skinner, G.J. & Allen, G.W. 1996 *Ants*. Naturalists' Handbooks No. 24. The Richmond Publishing Company, Slough.

Tolman, T. & Lewington, R. 2008 *Collins Butterfly Guide: The Most Complete Field Guide to the Butterflies of Britain and Europe*. Harper Collins, London.

Waring, P. & Townsend, M. 2009 *Field Guide to the Moths of Great Britain and Ireland*. 2nd edition. British Wildlife Publishing, Gillingham, Dorset.

Modern farming: without wildlife

Modern farming: with wildlife

Linnets and goldfinches, Halnaker Mill, West Sussex
In late summer, the seed-heads of common knapweed provide a food source for goldfinches and linnets.

Stonehenge, Wiltshire
An autumn grassland scene near Stonehenge, Wiltshire. Fieldfares, mistle thrushes, lapwings and a
solitary kestrel are all visible.